'Where's y
demanded h
his arms.

He continued, 'If I have
in all the doors—I'll be forced to make love to
you here…'

'I thought you could find any woman's
bedroom…just like a homing pigeon coming to
roost!' Alex giggled, waving him towards a
room at the end of the corridor.

'Damned cheek! It's high time I taught you
some manners,' Leo growled in rough, unlover-
like tones as he strode swiftly down the passage
into her room.

'Oh, yeah?' she laughed. 'You'll be lucky!'

'You're right…' he agreed quietly, as he gazed
down at the glinting blue eyes and soft
trembling lips; the thick mane of fair, sun-
bleached hair, and the high, firm breasts of her
slim figure. 'I'm definitely a *very* lucky man!'

Mary Lyons was born in Toronto, Canada, moving to live permanently in England when she was six, although she still proudly maintains her Canadian citizenship. Having married and raised four children, her life nowadays is relatively peaceful—unlike her earlier years when she worked as a radio announcer, reviewed books and, for a time, lived in a turbulent area of the Middle East. She still enjoys a bit of excitement, combining romance with action, humour and suspense in her books whenever possible.

Recent titles by the same author:

THE VALENTINE AFFAIR!

BY
MARY LYONS

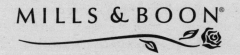

MILLS & BOON®

All the characters in this book have no existence outside the imagination of the author, and have no relation whatsoever to anyone bearing the same name or names. They are not even distantly inspired by any individual known or unknown to the author, and all the incidents are pure invention.

First published in Great Britain 1997
Harlequin Mills & Boon Limited,
Eton House, 18-24 Paradise Road, Richmond, Surrey TW9 1SR

© Mary Lyons 1997

ISBN 0 263 80608 1

Set in Times Roman 10½ on 12 pt.
01-9802-51295 C1

Printed and bound in Great Britain
by Mackays of Chatham PLC, Chatham

CHAPTER ONE

The London Chronicle Monday 4th February

JAMES BOSWELL'S SOCIAL DIARY

MARRIED BLISS...?

FOLLOWERS of the social scene will be interested to hear that glamorous, wickedly attractive Leo Hamilton (pictured right at a polo match) has finally met his fate...and is set to marry Fiona Bliss, 26, heiress of the 'Bliss Margarine' fortune.

Mega-rich banker Leo, 31—who gained a silver medal for fencing in the last Olympics, and is the son of society hostess Lady Lucas by her first marriage to the late Hon. Jack Hamilton—has up to now successfully avoided the clutches of matrimony, despite being linked in the past with so many beautiful women.

However, I am reliably informed that the happy couple will announce their engagement at next week's St Valentine's Ball—organised by Lady Lucas in aid of the National Society for Orphaned Children.

Leo and Fiona were unavailable for comment, but Fiona's mother, Ethel Bliss, is said to be 'delighted and very happy'.

The silver-grey Porsche made its way carefully through the crowded streets of the City of London, before coming to a halt outside a large, old Victorian building, currently the headquarters of the Hamilton banking empire.

'She's all yours, Benson,' the tall, dark-haired man drawled, unfolding his long limbs from the low-slung vehicle and tossing the car keys to the commissionaire, before visibly wincing at the sound as he slammed the door shut.

'Had a hard night, Mr Hamilton...?'

'A real blinder!' Leo agreed with a tired grin, before striding quickly up the steps and into the building.

'Ah, there you are, Mr Hamilton,' his personal assistant called out, hurrying to meet him as he exited the lift on the first floor. 'Your uncle would like to see you at ten o'clock.'

'Did he say why?'

His assistant shook her head. 'Lord Hamilton's secretary merely passed on the message. Although it may have something to do with the press conference, which is now scheduled for eleven-thirty,' she said, almost running to keep up with his long stride as she consulted the notepad in her hand. 'Your mother has phoned, and is most anxious to contact you. And...and I'd like to offer my own warmest congratulations. I'm sure you'll both be very happy.'

'Mmm...?' Leo shot her a brief, puzzled glance as he entered the blessed sanctuary of his office. Throwing his briefcase onto a black leather sofa, he sank down into the large, comfortable chair behind his desk.

'OK, Dora—hold all phone calls until I've had at least two cups of black coffee. On second thoughts,' he added with a tired smile, 'maybe you'd better just keep the black coffee flowing until further notice. And if you can find my dark sunglasses I'll promise to love you for ever!' he groaned, leaning back in the chair and closing his eyes.

'It looks as though it was some celebration party last night,' Dora said some minutes later, placing a cup and saucer on the desk in front of him.

'You're so right,' Leo agreed with a heavy sigh, and wondering—not for the first time—why on earth he'd agreed to attend Alan Morton's stag night which, starting on Friday night, had continued for most of the weekend. It was beginning to look as if his mother had been right when she'd accused him of getting too old for all-night rave-ups chiefly composed of wine, women and song. Maybe it really was time that he settled down to a life of quiet domesticity…?

'Are these what you're looking for?' his assistant asked, handing him a pair of dark glasses.

'Dora—you're an angel! What would I do without you?'

Gazing down at the tall, handsome, lounging figure with a fond smile, Dora reflected that even now, when clearly suffering from a massive hangover, Leo Hamilton was far and away the most good-looking man she'd ever worked for.

Well over six feet tall, his lean, broad-shouldered figure was only part of his dark attraction. Recently returned from a skiing holiday, his tanned features were emphasised by the thick black wavy hair sweeping down over his well-shaped head to curl over the edge of his collar.

Although he was only aged thirty-one, there were several strands of silver amongst the dark hair at his tem-

ples. While the green eyes beneath their heavy lids, set
above an aquiline nose, only hinted at the sensuality
which was clearly evident in the curved line of his wide
mouth, she had no doubt that he was just about every
red-blooded woman's dream hero.

And definitely not boring, Dora reminded herself with
an inward grin. The apparent ease with which he managed to charm the socks off so many beautiful women
was truly astounding. As was the amount of money he
spent at the local florist!

It was strange, she reflected, how the past three years
seemed to have sped by in a flash. In fact, ever since Mr
Hamilton had joined the bank—originally founded by a
distant ancestor and now headed by his uncle, Lord
Hamilton—it seemed as if the old building had been hit
by a typhoon. Because while the outside world might
regard her boss as a mere social dilettante and fun-loving
playboy, those long-serving members of staff, such as
herself, definitely knew better.

As she'd told her husband, after reading about Mr
Hamilton's engagement in the paper at breakfast that
morning. 'Well, all I can say is—he might play hard,
but he works even harder.'

'Tell me about it!' her long-suffering partner had muttered. 'Maybe, now the bloke's getting married, you
won't have to stay so late at the office.'

However, as she returned now to the mountain of
paperwork in her own room, Dora had severe doubts on
that score. She definitely knew a workaholic when she
saw one. And, despite the recent addition of more sec-
retarial staff to cope with the ever-increasing workload,
Mr Hamilton continued to carve his way through a formidable amount of business.

'Maybe you can tell me what the hell's going on!' Leo ground out in exasperation, after summoning her back to his office a few minutes later. 'I've just had a weird phone conversation with my mother. Quite honestly, if I didn't know any better, I'd say that the old girl had been suddenly struck down with senile dementia!'

He brushed long, tanned fingers roughly through his dark hair. 'From what I could make out—and it wasn't easy—she seemed very excited about some engagement of mine. But, after looking through my diary, I can't find anything out of the ordinary. Can you throw any light on the subject?'

Dora gazed at him in astonishment for a moment, before giving a short gurgle of laughter.

'Oh, come on, Mr Hamilton! I know you like a good joke. But, since the news was in the paper this morning, I don't think there's much point in trying to keep it a secret, do you?'

'Keep *what* a secret...?'

'Why, your engagement, of course.' She beamed down at him. 'In fact, I'm sure that I speak for everyone here in the bank when I say that I wish you and the young lady every happiness in your forthcoming marriage, and...'

Her voice died away as her employer slowly removed his dark glasses to reveal glittering emerald-green eyes, now regarding her with a cold, stern expression from beneath their heavy lids.

'My "forthcoming marriage"...? Well, I must say that sounds very interesting,' he drawled in a dangerously soft voice. 'However, since we both know that I'm suffering from a monumental hangover, I wonder if you would be kind enough to tell me just *who* I'm apparently supposed to be marrying.'

'Well, I thought…the report in the paper clearly stated that… I mean, I wouldn't normally have dreamed of saying anything, but there it was in black and white, and…'

'Hold it!' He gave a heavy sigh. 'Why don't you sit down, and let's take it from the top, hmm?

'Thank you, Dora,' Leo said a few minutes later. 'I think that I've now got the picture.' With a stony expression on his face, he waited for his assistant to leave the room before picking up the telephone on his desk.

'Ah, Fiona…?' he drawled as his call was answered. 'I've just heard some interesting news about our ''forthcoming marriage''. I don't suppose you'd happen to know how such an item found its way into the newspapers…?' he enquired with hard irony, leaning back in his chair and gazing up at the ornate plaster ceiling.

'Oh, yes…you're absolutely right,' Leo murmured some moments later. 'I definitely think we should have a meeting to discuss our engagement—and as soon as possible!'

Feeling like death warmed up, Alex Pemberton gazed around the large room, relieved to note that she wasn't the only one present at this Monday morning editorial conference who was looking somewhat the worse for wear. Thanks to the flu epidemic—which had swept through the newspaper office like one of the plagues of Egypt—she'd done virtually no work for the past ten days, and wasn't looking forward to being cross-examined by her editor, Mike Tanner.

While she waited for Mike to bring the meeting to

order, Alex was still wondering why she'd been asked to join the editorial conference. Such meetings were normally only attended by the *Chronicle*'s most senior journalists—not small-fry, junior members of the staff, such as herself.

However, Mike Tanner was clearly a law unto himself. His appointment as editor of the *London Chronicle* just over six months ago had brought about a completely new, dynamic wind of change in the newsroom.

Head-hunted by the paper's owners, Mike had obviously been appointed to rescue the falling circulation of what had once been a quality newspaper but which, over the years, had become both old-fashioned and outmoded. So far Mike seemed to have been achieving brilliant results, and was clearly determined to give the other tabloids a run for their money.

Having only joined the paper a few months before the new editor, Alex knew that she was incredibly lucky to have survived the brutally ruthless purge which had swiftly followed Mike Tanner's arrival. Since her only previous experience had been working for local, suburban weekly newspapers, she'd been quite certain that she was going to be sacked—just another minor casualty amongst so many of the older, well-known journalists.

But, when called to his office, she'd been surprised to find that she still had a job. And even more amazed to discover that Mike had found time, amidst the hectic schedule of his first week in charge of the paper, to check up on her work to date.

'I liked the angle you took on the trials and tribulations of being a pop star's wife. And that piece on the reclusive millionaire wasn't at all bad, either,' he'd told her, before adding with a grim smile, 'A pity you missed the fact that he was getting married for the fifth time only two days after the article was printed.'

'I know,' she'd admitted with a sigh. 'I felt such a fool!'

However, Mike had merely barked, 'We've all slipped up once or twice at the start of our careers. Just make sure it doesn't happen again.'

'I will,' she'd promised fervently, not only overjoyed at finding herself still in gainful employment, but thrilled to be appointed as a regular feature writer for the paper's magazine supplement. In fact, the only fly in the ointment was having to work with ghastly Imogen Hall-Knightly. If only...

'Right. Let's get this show on the road.' Mike's harsh, grating voice brought her abruptly back to the present.

Removing a large, fat cigar from between his lips, he blew a thick cloud of grey, evil-smelling smoke down the long table. 'I've called you all here today because I'm not happy with our circulation figures. Yes, they're rising,' he added over a muttered protest, 'but not as fast as I'd like. And, as I've already told Miz Imogen ''all-nightly'', here, I'm definitely not at all happy with our Saturday magazine.'

Alex struggled to keep her face straight as the older woman's lips tightened into an angry line.

Recently appointed as a deputy editor in charge of the weekend magazine—a glossy supplement entitled, *The Chronicle on Saturday*—Imogen was already a highly unpopular member of staff. Despite having gained a reputation as a first-class journalist, she'd managed to rub just about everyone up the wrong way. And Mike Tanner—fiercely proud of his poor, working-class background—seemed to take a delight in mispronouncing the surname of a woman he considered a raving snob.

'And just what, in your opinion, is wrong with the magazine?' Imogen demanded angrily.

'Just about everything,' Mike snapped. 'But mostly it's become too damn boring! It needs some zing and pizzazz…plus a lot more human interest articles. It certainly doesn't need reviews of a book on some obscure philosophy about which our readers know little and care less.'

'There's no harm in trying to educate our readers, surely?'

'Education?' Mike exploded, chomping violently on his cigar. 'What our readers want is *entertainment*—and don't you forget it!

'But, leaving aside the magazine for a moment, just look at what we've got in today's edition of the *Chronicle*,' he continued, jabbing an angry figure down at the newspaper open on the table in front of him. 'I'm ashamed to be the editor of such rubbish!'

There was a deathly silence as Mike glared around the table before pointing a stubby nicotine-yellowed finger at the girl sitting next to Alex. 'I want a radical overhaul of the fashion page, Tessa. And as quickly as possible!'

'Er…right,' Tessa muttered nervously. 'What exactly did you have in mind?'

'Well, for starters, like every other red-blooded man, I'm sick and tired of those ultra-thin models—who look more like stick insects than living human beings. I'll give you double the spread if you can find some women with a decent bust.'

Tessa grinned. 'Your word is my command, Mike. Nothing under a 36C—right?'

'I'm glad that at least someone around here has got the message!' He threw a malicious grin at Imogen, before turning to the City editor. 'OK, Ben—I want less of those boring share tips, and a lot more about financial scams in high places. Now, I hear on the grapevine...'

Alex, who had little interest in City gossip, took the opportunity to beg some aspirins from Tessa. 'I was feeling a lot better earlier this morning. But I can't seem to get rid of this thumping headache.'

'No problem,' the other girl murmured, opening her handbag and producing a small bottle of white pills. 'Hang on to them—I've got plenty more in my desk. I hope you feel better soon.'

'So do I.' Alex smiled ruefully as she poured some water into a glass from the carafe on the table and swallowed the aspirins. 'Especially since I haven't even managed to read a newspaper for the past week.'

'Well, you'd better catch up as fast as possible,' Tessa cautioned softly. 'Because, while it looks as though I've got off fairly lightly, I hear Mike is out for blood. And woe betide anyone who can't come up with at least one brilliant, sparkling idea for a new feature.'

'Thanks for the gypsy's warning,' Alex muttered, brushing a hand through her thick mane of dark blonde hair and desperately trying to pummel her brain into thinking of something as their editor's voice rose several decibels.

'You'll have to do better than this—or you'll be out on your ear!' Mike was roaring at James Boswell, the editor of the social diary.

'Research shows that our readers like nothing better than a really juicy divorce, political sex scandals—or reading about high jinks in royal circles,' he continued grimly. 'So why give them this feeble piece about some idle-rich banker who's decided to get married to a margarine heiress?'

'Well, I had a hot tip...'

The editor gave a loud exclamation of disgust. 'As far as I can see it's totally uninteresting. There's nothing exciting about *margarine*, for heaven's sake. Why should our readers give a toss about this guy? I'm sorry, James—but you're going to have to do a whole lot "butter" than this!'

James swallowed hard. 'Actually, it is an interesting piece of news,' he maintained stubbornly, over the rumble of laughter which had greeted his editor's pun.

'Mainly because the man in question is a regular Casanova,' James continued, a distinct note of envy in his voice. 'I'm told he's got more luscious, stunning-looking girls queuing up to jump into his bed than I've had hot dinners! So, the news that he's finally decided to take the plunge into matrimony is going to make a lot of glamorous, well-known women *very* unhappy.'

'OK, OK, maybe there is a story there,' Mike grudgingly agreed. 'But, if the guy has really been such a stud, why didn't you say so in words of one syllable? Why bother with all this "avoided the clutches of matrimony" nonsense, when what this piece clearly needs is some quotes from angry, disgruntled ex-girlfriends?'

As the other man muttered some excuse about the laws of libel and the difficulty in getting anything past the *Chronicle*'s lawyers, Tessa gave Alex a quick nudge.

'James is right. That's definitely what I call a nice piece of male crumpet,' she whispered, grinning as she passed Alex her copy of the paper, open at the social page.

Pointing to the picture of a handsome, dark-haired man standing beside his horse at a polo match, Tessa added with a giggle, 'I always go for men dressed in sexy, skin-tight breeches. In fact, he can leave those long leather riding boots outside my bedroom door any night he pleases!'

But, strangely, Alex didn't seem to be listening to her friend's comments, her face growing pale as she stared fixedly down at the newsprint in front of her.

'My dear boy.' Lord Hamilton beamed at his nephew. 'I don't suppose I'm the first person to congratulate you on the news of your engagement. However, I'm very pleased to hear that you've decided to settle down, at last.'

'Well, the truth is...'

'The truth is that I was becoming a little worried about you,' the older man told him sternly. 'Quite frankly, it hasn't done this bank any good to have the gossip columns carrying reports of your idle, loose behaviour.'

'Oh, come on, Uncle!' Leo gave a snort of wry laughter. 'I hardly see myself as some sort of Lothario. In fact, most of the stuff printed in the newspapers was complete moonshine!'

'Of course, I've nothing against young men sowing their wild oats.'

'I should think not,' Leo grinned. 'Especially when, according to my mother, you painted the town red in your younger days.'

'Yes, well...that was a long time ago.' The older man gave his nephew a slightly sheepish smile. 'As you know, I've been happily married to your aunt Emily for the past thirty years. Which is why,' he added firmly,

'I'm relieved to know that you've clearly decided to settle down and put that sort of life well behind you.'

Wishing that he didn't feel quite so mentally sluggish, and wondering how to explain that his future wasn't *quite* as clear-cut as his uncle seemed to think, Leo was forestalled as Lord Hamilton rose to his feet.

'The thing is, dear boy, for some time I've been wanting to make you a full partner and director of this bank. So, following the good news this morning, I've already had a few words with most of the other members of the board, and they've all agreed to your appointment.'

'Hang on!' Leo interjected swiftly. 'I'd like to discuss this matter a lot more thoroughly before you take any action. The thing is, I'm not exactly... Well, the fact is...'

'My doctors have been telling me that I should slow down and think about retirement,' the older man continued, ignoring the younger man's words as he walked over to the large window in his office and stared down at the traffic below. 'And, having no children of my own, it's a great relief to know that my own nephew will eventually be succeeding me as managing director.'

'I'm really very flattered that you think I could do the job,' Leo assured him. 'And I do understand that you'd like a member of the family to continue as head of this bank. However, your colleagues may well feel—with a certain amount of justice—that I'm far too young for the job. Not to mention the fact that it could well appear to be a bad case of nepotism.'

'Nonsense!' His uncle turned around to face him. 'You've worked very hard over the past few years, and fully earned your spurs.'

'Surely there's no need to make a decision straight

away?' Leo protested, desperately wishing that his head didn't feel as if it was full of cotton wool. 'I mean I'd like to have some time to think about it, and...'

'There's nothing to think about,' his uncle stated firmly, walking back to his desk and gathering papers together as his secretary came into the room, followed by two assistants. 'Now, I mustn't keep the board waiting. Maybe we can have a word later this afternoon?'

'But, I really do need to talk to you...'

'Later, dear boy. Later...' Lord Hamilton muttered, hurrying out of the room.

Swearing under his breath with baffled frustration, Leo wandered slowly back to his own office, quite unable to see how he was going to extricate himself from what was rapidly becoming a *very* complicated situation.

Alex glanced cautiously down the table, relieved to see that Mike Tanner was now leaning back in his chair, happily puffing on his second cigar of the morning, and regarding with satisfaction the pale faces and cowed figures around the table.

Her editor obviously believed that putting the fear of God into his staff helped to keep them on their toes in what was an ever-increasingly tough and competitive market. And, to be fair, he wasn't far short of the mark. Threatened with the risk of losing their jobs, it was amazing how many new, creative and exciting ideas had been put forward during the past hour.

Unfortunately, Alex's brain had obstinately refused to come up with anything that Mike would regard as creative, let alone interesting. The fact that she'd escaped unscathed so far didn't mean a damn thing, since Alex knew that she would soon be in the firing line. Why else would Mike have demanded her attendance at this morning's editorial meeting, when such conferences were only normally attended by the paper's leading journalists?

Desperately sipping the dregs of her by now cold coffee, Alex waited for Armageddon to strike. And, sure enough, it wasn't long in coming.

'Now, Miss Pemberton,' the editor growled from his position at the head of the table. 'I don't think we've heard from you this morning. Have you, by any chance, got some new articles in the pipeline?'

'Well, er...no, not really,' she confessed. 'I'm still working on the St Valentine's Day feature, of course, but...'

'Ah, yes...I've had some thoughts on that subject.' Mike drew deeply on his cigar. 'Since the fourteenth of February falls on a Thursday this year, I've decided that the whole of that Saturday's magazine will be devoted to the subject of love and romance. You know the sort of thing...' He waved expansively in the air. 'Why women expect men to propose to them on that day, some sexy fashion articles, how to cook a wonderful dinner for the man of your dreams, et cetera, et cetera.'

There was a general chorus of approval around the table, with the more sycophantic journalists crying, 'Great,' 'Brilliant,' 'A real winner.' The only dissenting voice was that of Imogen Hall-Knightly, clearly furious at the way Mike was hijacking her editorial control of the magazine supplement.

'It sounds *just* the sort of rubbish you'd find in those awful women's magazines—or in the worst of the downmarket tabloids,' she rasped. 'And, I find it very offensive that you should wish to promote such a stereotyped view of women—reinforcing their role as mere play-things of the male species!'

There was a startled hush following her words, during which everyone held their breath, fully expecting their editor to verbally rip the deeply disliked Imogen into small, tiny pieces.

However, they were startled when Mike merely leaned back in his seat and, quite astonishingly, gave the rigidly angry woman a bland smile.

'Well, you may be right. We certainly don't want to be accused of being politically incorrect, or of discrimination against men—do we?'

'Er…yes…no…I mean…' Imogen gasped, frantically waving away the thick cloud of evil-smelling cigar smoke which the editor had just puffed in her direction.

'Which is why,' Mike continued imperturbably, 'I've decided to include a feature, written by Alex Pemberton, which will be solely devoted to the male point of view. I rather fancy the title, "Sex and the single man." How does that grab you?'

'By the throat!' Imogen ground out angrily, amidst the sound of general laughter.

'That can be arranged,' her editor drawled menacingly, pausing for a moment before turning to look down the table. 'OK, Alex, what have you got so far?'

Stunned by the abrupt turn of events, Alex struggled to pull herself together. Was this the chance of a lifetime, or what? There was a small problem, of course, because her outline wasn't nearly complete. But maybe she could skim over the gaps? It was definitely worth a try, she decided quickly, taking a deep breath and hoping for the best.

'I love the title,' she told Mike with a grin. 'And

everything I've done so far will fit in very well with what you want. As you know, before being struck down by flu I was working on a St Valentine's Day feature...'

'We've gathered that much,' Mike snapped irritably. 'Get on with it!'

'OK...OK,' Alex muttered nervously. 'Well, I decided to write about three couples—working-class, middle-class, and upper-class, rich socialites—pointing out the differences in their romantic lifestyles. I've already got a plumber and his girlfriend, plus a tax inspector and his fiancée who are all quite happy to co-operate on the feature. The idea is to examine, in depth, what Imogen might well refer to as their ''mating rituals''.'

Ignoring the general laughter, Imogen scowled down the table at Alex—a fact which didn't disturb the younger girl in the slightest. She was fed up to the back teeth with Imogen's continual sniping comments—mainly concerned with what she regarded as Alex's rich, privileged background—and deeply resented the older woman's inability to judge her work on its merits.

'I'm planning to interview them all separately, as well as together,' Alex continued blithely, before being struck by a sudden idea. 'By the way, it's just occurred to me that I might be able to take them all to a posh, up-market St Valentine's Day Ball—which is usually held in one of the grand London hotels. What do you think?' she asked Mike with a hopeful smile.

'The organisers always hold these balls on the *actual* day itself, which means it would be perfect for the following Saturday's supplement. So, I could write a second piece, mainly about what a good time they had in celebrating their romance.'

'Yeah…that's not a bad idea. Not a bad idea at all.' Her editor nodded. 'In fact, I reckon your idea for two bites at the cherry sounds very promising. I particularly like the idea of a plumber rubbing shoulders on an equal footing with some toffee-nosed Hooray Henry,' he added with a chuckle, gathering up his papers and announcing the close of the meeting.

As the other members of staff began leaving the room, Imogen—who, as an experienced journalist, never missed a trick—quickly seized an opportunity to cut the younger girl down to size.

'I'm quite sure that Miss Pemberton has done her homework,' she said with a cold, malicious smile. 'But I don't recall her mentioning any details about the third, upper-class couple…'

Alex, who'd been happily basking in the warmth of Mike's rare praise, felt a cold, hard lump of apprehension filling her stomach. Trust Imogen to wield the poisoned dagger!

'No, well…I hadn't quite sorted out the final details before being struck down by the flu,' she told him briskly, doing her best to sound businesslike and confident. 'It's just a matter of tying up a few loose ends, and—'

'We'll have to insist on knowing exactly *who* you've lined up,' Imogen interjected sharply, before turning to the editor. 'For this feature to work she's going to need a wealthy, well-known and socially prominent couple. It's really no good *dear* Alex relying, as she does so often, on the last-minute help of some of her idle, rich layabout friends…is it?'

'That woman's an absolute bitch!' Tessa muttered sympathetically as she rose from the table. 'Go for it, kid. Smash her in the eyes with some really glamorous names.'

Unfortunately Alex—only too well aware that she hadn't yet come up with any ideas for the upper-class pair of lovers—could only desperately pray for divine guidance, frantically cudgelling her brain in an effort to provide a satisfactory answer.

'Well?' her editor barked impatiently. 'Hurry up! We can't sit around here all morning, you know.'

Thinking about the episode later, Alex could only imagine that she'd been blindly trapped within the coils of some evil, malign influence. What else could have led her to commit an act of such folly? However, with her mind completely blank and just about to admit defeat, she found herself staring down at the newspaper open on the table in front of her.

Even as she raised her hand—pointing with a trembling finger to the picture of the man about whom Tessa had made such a crude joke—she could hear loud warning bells echoing in her head. But, as she ruefully acknowledged to herself later, both the sin of pride and an overwhelming, urgent need to escape from such a sticky situation proved to be irresistible.

'It's this man,' she said defiantly. 'I'm going to be featuring Leo Hamilton and his fiancée, Fiona Bliss.'

'Do me a favour!' James Boswell laughed scornfully, gathering up his papers and walking towards the door. 'You'll never get him to go along with it. Not in a month of Sundays!'

'That stupid girl has just plucked a name out of thin air!' Imogen agreed furiously. 'The Leo Hamiltons of this world would never agree to co-operate with us. He might just respond to an approach from *The Times*, for instance, but definitely not a down-market rag like the *London Chronicle*.'

'Thank you for those few kind words, Imogen!' Mike grated angrily, prevented from saying any more as James, about to leave the room, turned to underline the older woman's words.

'I hate to say it—but, unfortunately, Imogen's quite right,' he shrugged. 'I don't normally reveal my sources. However, it seems only fair to say that it was the girl's mother who tipped me off about the engagement. Believe me, Leo Hamilton would prefer to slit his own throat rather than court any publicity. And, as far as co-operation with this newspaper is concerned...?' He shrugged again. 'You're likely to get more information out of an oyster!'

'Hmm... Well, it looks as if I'll have to cancel the feature. Especially since there's not enough time to line up anyone else.' Mike nodded slowly in agreement. 'I'm very disappointed in you, Alex,' he added sternly. 'Why promise something you can't deliver?'

'I *can* deliver Leo Hamilton,' she told him firmly.

James Boswell smiled and shook his head. 'Come on, Alex! What's the point in flogging a dead horse? Everyone knows that both the guy and his family have always avoided any publicity like the plague. So, there's no way he's going to agree to participate in an article about his engagement. Right?'

'No, you're wrong,' she protested, before turning to her editor. 'I'll admit that James has a point—Leo Hamilton wouldn't normally be too happy about the idea. Well, not at first, anyway. But, *please* give me a break, Mike,' she begged earnestly. 'Because, in this particular case, I can virtually guarantee to bring home the bacon.'

'This is all a complete waste of time,' Imogen snapped. 'I don't know about you, Mike, but I've got better things to do than to listen to such nonsense.'

'Calm down, everyone,' the editor said firmly, before regarding the younger girl intently for a moment. 'You seem very certain that you won't have any problems with this article, right?'

'Right.'

'Now, you're certainly not stupid, Alex,' he continued slowly. 'You must know that if you want my backing I'm going to need some hard facts. What makes you so certain that you can gain the co-operation of this guy? Are *you* one of his ex-girlfriends, for instance?'

'Certainly not!' she snapped curtly.

'Well...?'

Alex hesitated for a moment, and then gave a heavy sigh. 'OK, Mike. I normally try to keep family and business matters entirely separate. However, if you're insisting on some ''hard facts''...' She shrugged. 'Well, it just so happens that Leo Hamilton is my stepbrother.'

CHAPTER TWO

'Go away—you great big bully!' Alex muttered angrily, impatiently tooting her horn at the driver of a large delivery truck who was clearly trying to force her small car out of the way as she drove through the narrow, crowded streets of the city.

Ever since the meeting in Mike Tanner's office only two hours ago it felt as though she'd been frantically spinning like a top. Which had, at least, the virtue of keeping her mind fully occupied, and unable to think too much about the forthcoming confrontation with Leo Hamilton.

But now as she pulled on the handbrake, staring blindly out through her windscreen at the lines of cars and trucks all firmly stalled in the heavy traffic, there seemed little she could do to combat the wild, nervous fluttering in her stomach.

Relax! Keep calm…there's no need to panic. Quite apart from anything else, there's a good chance that Leo probably won't even recognise you, she told herself firmly. 'And let's hope he doesn't!' she added out loud, with an attempt at grim humour, almost shuddering as she recalled the deeply unhappy young girl who had suddenly found herself dumped in a strange household in Italy all those years ago.

Most teenage girls looked a mess at one time or another—but she'd *really* gone to town, with that 'heavy Gothic' style!

It was difficult to remember now exactly what had prompted her to dye her hair jet-black. Or why she'd ever thought that smothering her face in chalky-white foundation and applying both sooty-black mascara and dark crimson lipstick with a heavy hand could be a good idea. Could it have been some sort of protest? An infantile act of rebellion against an unkind world? If so, it had, most unfortunately, proved to be a fatal mistake.

After one appalled glance at the strange-looking sixteen-year-old girl who'd suddenly arrived at her holiday home in Tuscany, Leo's mother, Eleanor Lucas, had swiftly taken matters in hand. However, by the time she'd forcefully bullied Alex into looking more like the girl's normal self, it had proved to be far, far too late. Because, barely moments after setting eyes on him, Alex had fallen desperately in love with her tall, dark and handsome twenty-three-year-old stepbrother. While he, for his part, had clearly only thought of her as some ghastly teenaged version of one of the Munsters.

Over the years, Alex had done her level best to forget that long, baking-hot and totally dreadful summer holiday, where one disaster had been swiftly followed by another, like a Greek tragedy. But now, with the prospect of meeting once more the man who had so blighted her young life, she could feel her skin almost crawling with embarrassment and humiliation.

Cool it! she told herself firmly as the stalled traffic began slowly moving, at last. Just about everyone makes a complete idiot of themselves at least once in their lives. So, why should you be the exception? Besides, what happened in the past doesn't matter. It's the here and now that's important. And, if you don't want to find

yourself out of a job, you've *got* to get this story—come
hell or high water!

Unfortunately, trying to psych herself up for the forthcoming confrontation with Leo wasn't proving too successful. Mainly because it didn't need a very high IQ to
realise that, after the horrendous scene in Mike's office,
her job was now squarely on the line. A fact which her
editor had made crystal clear.

'I'm going out on a limb for you, Alex. So you'd
better deliver the goods,' he'd warned.

Ignoring Imogen's furious anger at being overruled,
Mike had continued grimly, 'These articles of yours had
better be damn good. If I find that you've been spinning
a yarn—or trying to pull the wool over my eyes in any
way—I can guarantee that you'll *never* work for me
again. Or any other newspaper, for that matter. Got the
message?'

Alex had nodded nervously, the noise of Imogen's
rage and fury ringing in her ears as she'd hurried away
from his office.

Well, at least she hadn't been lying about her relationship with Leo Hamilton, Alex had comforted herself,
trying to ignore her guilty conscience as she'd reached
the sanctuary of her desk.

Oh, yeah? Just *who* do you think you're kidding? The
ghostly voice in her head had demanded with a scornful
laugh. You may not have told a one hundred per cent
lie. But you were definitely being economical with the
truth—right? Because Leo is only a sort of stepbrother—
or should it be stepbrother by marriage? And you
haven't set eyes on the rotten man, or the rest of his
horrid family, for almost eight years.

'OK...OK,' she'd muttered under her breath, resolutely banishing her conscience to the far, dark recesses of her mind as she'd tried to concentrate on the Herculean task before her.

First and foremost Alex had realised that she needed a lot of background information—almost as important to a journalist as water in the Sahara Desert. After all, she knew absolutely nothing about Fiona Bliss, and had virtually no knowledge of what her stepbrother had been up to during the past eight years.

However, just over an hour later, she'd been feeling quite pleased with herself. The *Chronicle*'s library had produced a pile of news cuttings on Leo and his family, while a quick phone call to her old school friend Sophie would hopefully provide a whole host of material about his new fiancée, Fiona Bliss.

Unfortunately, Sophie—who rented the basement flat of Alex's house, and worked on a glamorous monthly magazine mostly devoted to fashion and the lives of those prominent in society—had proved an unexpectedly hard nut to crack. It was only after promising to lend the other girl her best long gown for a deathly smart St Valentine's Ball—*and* her favourite pair of high-heeled gold sandals and matching bag—that Sophie had reluctantly agreed to raid the files in her office.

'Great!' Alex had grinned down the phone. 'So, how about meeting me for a late lunch in the pub around the corner from your office, and you can give me the details then. OK?'

'No, it's not OK,' her friend had protested. 'I'll need a lot more time than just a few hours. Who do you think I am? Mata Hari?'

Alex had gritted her teeth in frustration. 'Look…do you want to be the belle of the ball, and make that ex-boyfriend of yours as jealous as hell, or what?' she demanded. 'Of course, if you're happy to wear your tatty old black dress, and don't mind looking like something the cat dragged in…'

'Oh, *all right*!' Sophie had ground out, before slamming down her phone.

So far, so good. But with so little time in which to both complete her interviews and write the article, Alex knew that time was of the essence. Which was why, striving to keep calm and banish her rising panic, she'd swallowed her pride and begged James Boswell for his help.

Clearly aggrieved that he hadn't known of her relationship to Leo Hamilton, the paper's social editor still didn't think she had much of a chance of gaining the glamorous banker's co-operation.

'Especially now that the guy has the modern equivalent of a shotgun wedding in front of him,' James had added with a sour grin.

'You don't mean…?'

'No, of course I don't think his girlfriend is pregnant,' he'd retorted curtly. 'But your stepbrother is going to find it almost impossible to extricate himself from the clutches of Fiona's mother, Ethel Bliss. Believe me, that's one really tough, hard woman—who's ruthlessly ambitious for her only child. Don't forget, it was Ethel who tipped me off about the ''engagement''. So, even if Leo wanted to extricate himself from the situation— and I've no reason to think that he does—I'll lay any money that he's going to find himself standing at the altar, firmly anchored to a heavy ball and chain!'

James had also let fall the information that her step-

brother lived in a large, glamorous penthouse apartment
in Knightsbridge, overlooking Hyde Park.

'With a tough doorman, and more intruder alarms than
the Bank of England, none of my contacts has been able
to put a foot over the threshold. I still don't think Leo
will agree to help with your article,' he'd added, with a
bad-tempered shrug. 'But, since you're a member of the
family, at least getting in to see the guy will be a piece
of cake, right?'

'Er…right,' she'd murmured, hoping she'd sounded
more confident than she felt, and quickly realising that
her only hope was to try and catch Leo off guard, in his
office at the bank.

'Nothing ventured—nothing gained!' Alex now told
herself firmly. But, as she drove slowly past the Mansion
House, keeping a sharp lookout for a space in which to
park her car, she couldn't help worrying about the forthcoming interview.

After a frantic dash home to change out of the jeans
which she normally wore in the newspaper office, Alex
still wasn't at all sure whether she'd picked the right sort
of 'stuffy' outfit. Maybe the black wool suit, with its
tightly fitted jacket over sheer black stockings and high-
heeled black court shoes, was a bit *too* funereal for a
bank?

Still…what the heck? she told herself defiantly as she
finally managed to find a free parking meter. Because,
quite frankly, the chances of her actually managing to
get as far as Leo's office were so slim as to be practically
anorexic!

In fact, even getting through the bank's front door was
likely to be almost impossible, she realised, walking
slowly up the street towards the large Victorian building,

and noting the figure of a burly, uniformed commission-aire filling the doorway. Desperately trying to suppress the sudden urge to turn tail and buy a one-way ticket to South America, Alex gradually noticed that a steady stream of people seemed to be approaching the bank.

Surely that wasn't…? Oh, wow! It really was turning out to be her lucky day, she told herself with a slightly hysterical giggle, before running swiftly across the road.

'Hi, Ben,' she smiled breathlessly at the *Chronicle*'s financial editor.

'Good heavens! What on earth are you doing in this neck of the woods, Alex? I didn't know you were inter-ested in City finance.'

'Of course I'm interested,' she assured him earnestly, firmly clutching hold of his arm. 'In fact, I find the whole concept of world trade simply *fascinating*!'

'That's great!' he exclaimed, his cheeks flushing slightly as he gallantly led her up the steps. 'Today's meeting is only a public relations exercise. But it will be interesting to hear more details of Hamilton's partial merger with a German bank.'

'Absolutely!' she agreed, almost unable to believe her luck. If she could swan in with Ben, she was almost home and dry!

'So, after we've heard what they've got to say, maybe you'd let me take you out to lunch? I'm writing a feature on some recent corporate takeovers, which I think you'll find quite thought provoking.'

'Oh, dear—I don't think I can make lunch,' Alex mur-mured, softening the blow with a beaming smile as they walked up the steps. 'But I'm looking forward to reading your article. It sounds absolutely *riveting*!' she added, both amazed and slightly ashamed at her sudden, un-expected ability to lie her head off.

'Here we are,' he announced as they approached the open door of the bank. 'Got your press card?'

'Of course.' She flashed the small plastic folder at the commissionaire, who happily waved them onwards into the large building.

Hoping to remain as inconspicuous as possible, Alex led Ben to the far side of the room, where rows of gilt chairs were set well back, facing a large table at the other end.

Staring up at the amount of gold leaf on the ornately decorated ceiling, she let her gaze move on to take in the enormous glass chandelier, clearly lit to banish the grey February morning beyond the windows, around which were draped thick crimson brocade curtains. In fact—with its dark crimson plush covered walls heavily encrusted with large gloomy oil paintings—it looked more like a gentlemen's club or a grand drawing room than a modern working environment.

Well, well! It certainly looked as if these merchant bankers believed in making themselves very comfort-able. Nice work if you can get it! Alex mused causti-cally, wondering how soon she could slip out of the room and continue her search for Leo Hamilton.

While she had been taking stock of her luxurious sur-roundings, the room had been gradually filling up with journalists from most of the daily newspapers and those magazines concerned with finance. Busy chatting to one another, it wasn't until two men walked through a door at the far end of the room that the general conversation ceased and the audience began taking out their notebooks.

Seated behind a large, stout figure in a gabardine raincoat, Alex had difficulty in seeing what was going on.
However, as soon as she moved her chair slightly, giving
herself a better view of the table at the end of the room,
she realised with a jolt that—thanks to Ben—there was
no need for her to seek out Leo Hamilton.

That he hadn't changed at all was the first coherent
thought to emerge from the swirling chaos in her mind.
But then, as her vision cleared, Alex realised that she
was mistaken.

It was now nearly eight years since she'd last seen
Leo, and, while his outward, extraordinarily handsome
appearance might seem little altered, he now clearly saw
no reason to hide his obvious command of the situation,
or the overpowering strength of his forceful personality.
He had, in fact, matured into a tough, resourceful man,
and it didn't look as if nowadays that firm, hard mouth
laughed very much, if at all.

The bright light from the chandelier cast a sheen on
his dark hair, highlighting a few threads of silver at the
temples. His skin was very tanned, as if he spent most
of his time in the open air—not the usual environment
for a banker. Or that of a man who, if James Boswell
was to be believed, apparently spent a great deal of his
time in the bedrooms of beautiful women!

But clearly that aspect of his life had been left aside
as he calmly welcomed members of the press. In fact,
Leo's tall figure appeared perfectly relaxed—the wide,
powerful shoulders and lean hips accentuated by the im-
maculate formality of his well-cut, dark grey lounge
suit—as he smoothly explained the reasons behind his
bank's new merger with a German financial institution.
Watching the cool, unruffled way in which he dealt with

a host of questions from the assembled journalists, Alex had no problem in understanding why he'd been chosen to present this exercise in public relations.

But, while Leo appeared to be exuding an air of relaxed charm, he didn't succeed in fooling *her*…not for one minute! Because, as she knew only too well, beneath the suave and charming exterior Leo Hamilton had always been as hard as tungsten steel.

The perfect example of an iron fist clothed in a soft velvet glove, Alex reminded herself grimly, unable to prevent an icy shiver of apprehension from feathering down her spine.

Buried in unhappy memories, it was some moments before she realised that the meeting was breaking up. Noting that, while one or two journalists were busy checking some final points with Leo, the majority of those present were slowly leaving the room, she muttered a brief goodbye to Ben before mingling with the crowd as they made their way out through the door.

One swift, rapid glance around the large foyer was enough for Alex to see that she'd have to move sharply if she wished to avoid attracting the attention of either the receptionists or the commissionaire, who was now carefully shepherding the press corps out of the building. Using a group of journalists as a shield, she edged towards the bank of lifts, slipping inside and quickly punching a button at random.

'Hello, Dora,' she called out some minutes later, having charmed a passing office boy into giving her not only the exact location of Leo's office but also the name of his personal assistant. 'I've just popped in to see Leo. Is it all right if I wait in his office?'

Glancing up from her desk, Dora stared at the slim figure standing in the open doorway.

Quite certain that she'd never seen this person before, Dora was also well aware of Mr Hamilton's inflexible rule that girlfriends were *never* allowed anywhere near his office. And, since no respectable office would dream of employing anyone with that untamed cloud of fair, sun-bleached hair tumbling down around her shoulders—not to mention one wearing such a disgracefully short black skirt over long slim legs encased in sheer black stockings—she clearly didn't work here, at the bank.

However, just as Dora was about to pick up the phone and call Security, she took another, hard look at the girl leaning casually against the door. You didn't have to be a serious follower of fashion to realise that suit must have cost a fortune. And those Gucci shoes and matching handbag on its gold chain wouldn't have been exactly cheap, either. So…

Oh, heavens! It looked as though she'd nearly made a dreadful mistake. Because, of course, this extraordinarily attractive-looking girl must be Mr Hamilton's new fiancée.

'I'm sorry, I didn't realise…' Dora muttered, rising quickly from behind her desk. 'It's Miss Fiona Bliss, isn't it?'

'How did you guess?' Alex smiled happily at the older woman. 'Er…darling Leo is just finishing a meeting downstairs. So, is it all right if I wait for him in his office?'

'Of course.' Dora beamed at the girl and led her into the palatial room. 'Can I get you anything?'

'I'd sell my soul for a cup of coffee,' Alex admitted

with a grin, waiting until Leo's secretary had left the room before sinking down into a leather chair.

'Phew!' she muttered with relief a little while later, gratefully sipping her hot coffee—and thankful that she didn't have to go through such an exhausting charade every day of the week. What a piece of luck, his secretary mistaking her for Leo's fiancée! Although exactly what she was going to say or do when he returned to his office, she had absolutely no idea.

However, while she had the chance, maybe she ought to have a good look around his office? If her articles were going to be a success, it was important to try to pick up some clues about both his present lifestyle and his new fiancée.

Unfortunately, there was virtually nothing in Leo's opulent suite of rooms which couldn't just as well have been found in the office of any highly successful man— a huge leather-covered mahogany desk with its back to the large window, a grey and white marble mantelpiece over a fake log fire, comfortable black leather chairs and sofa... It all looked depressingly bare of clues. Apart from the fact that there were no photographs, of course. That was definitely odd. Surely he ought to have a picture of his beloved fiancée placed prominently on his desk?

Her thoughts were interrupted by the sound of firm footsteps approaching down the marble-floored corridor. Bracing herself for the forthcoming confrontation, Alex heard his secretary informing Leo that his fiancée was waiting for him in his office.

'Oh, really...?' a deep voice queried sardonically, before the door was thrown open and Leo Hamilton walked into the room.

He paused on the threshold, his hard green eyes flicking quickly over the figure of the girl by the fireplace, and Alex held her breath as she stared at the tall, broad-shouldered figure in the doorway.

It was one thing to have viewed this man across the length of the large room downstairs a few minutes ago. But quite another to find herself now standing only a few feet away from Leo's tall, dominant figure—and almost reeling from the forceful impact of his dark, physical attraction.

How could she have forgotten…? Why hadn't she remembered the devastating aura of sheer, raw sex appeal projected by this man, who was now studying her with such calm detachment on his handsome, tanned face?

Desperately trying to control a hot flush rising over her cheeks, and the quivers of awareness scorching through her body, she put out a hand to clutch hold of the mantelpiece for support. Fearful memories of their last encounter were now welling up inside her like a sudden sickness, and Alex could feel herself trembling as if in the grip of a fierce tropical fever.

She should never have come here! What on earth had possessed her to even contemplate such folly?

But Leo's gaze of cool, calm uninterest helped to steady her nerves. She held her breath, watching as he gave a slight, dismissive shrug of his shoulders and began moving across the thick carpet towards his large desk by the window. It was some moments before she realised that, despite her own strong, almost overwhelming response to his presence, he apparently had no recognition of the girl staring at him so intently.

'It would seem to be my lucky day for collecting "fiancées"!' Leo drawled, sitting down and pulling out various drawers. 'However, if you can provide me with some aspirins, I'll seriously consider bestowing on you both my hand *and* my heart!'

Thrown completely off balance by this calm reaction to her unexpected presence in his office, Alex found herself giving a startled, involuntary gurgle of nervous laughter.

Obviously surprised by her response, he shot her a quick, penetrating glance, and continued to search through the drawers of his desk.

'I must say that I've had better offers in my time,' she told him with a grim smile, making a determined effort to pull herself together. 'But that definitely sounds an interesting proposal!' she added, opening her handbag and walking over to place Tessa's small bottle of white pills on his desk.

'Bless you,' he murmured, filling a glass from the carafe of water in front of him, and sighing deeply as he leaned back in his chair.

'Well, now...yes. I can imagine that you will have had several possibly better offers,' he drawled a few moments later, his gaze moving slowly over the tall, slim figure of the girl standing in front of him.

The intense, insulting thoroughness with which he scrutinised the cloud of sun-bleached hair, the high, firm breasts, and the length of her legs beneath the short skirt brought a flush to her cheeks and an angry sparkle to her wide blue eyes.

'It's no good glaring at me like that, my girl!' he grinned with sardonic amusement, clearly enjoying her discomfiture. 'Especially as we both know that you must have spun a complete yarn to poor Dora. And, since you most definitely are *not* Fiona Bliss, maybe you'd be good enough to tell me your name?'

She regarded him warily in silence, and then shrugged. 'I did wonder if you'd recognise me, after all this time. But clearly it would seem that you haven't.' She paused for a moment. 'I'm Alex Pemberton.'

He frowned, staring at her intently, before giving a shake of his dark head. 'No, sorry—I simply don't recall that name. And I'm very sure that I wouldn't have forgotten meeting you,' he added, once more allowing the green eyes beneath their heavy lids to slowly and carefully scrutinise her figure. '*Quite* certain, in fact!'

'Ah, well—that just goes to show how even the cleverest of men can be mistaken!'

Alex smiled blandly at him, suddenly feeling light-headed, and totally amazed to find that she wasn't frightened of this man after all.

So, OK…she had been startled and confused a few moments ago by the sudden, shocking reminder of his overwhelming sexual attraction. But she was now recovering fast, and couldn't think why, over the past eight years, she'd stupidly allowed Leo's dark image to become magnified in her mind until it had assumed the proportions of a nightmare.

She had, of course, been pathetically young and innocent at the time. But now, standing here in his office, everything seemed very different. For the first time in her life—certainly as far as this man was concerned—she was feeling quite extraordinarily confident, with no doubts about her ability to cope with the situation.

'I hear that you are about to become engaged. I imagine that must make your parents very happy,' Alex said,

casually sitting down on a Chippendale chair set in front
of his desk.

'I really don't see that the private life of myself, or
my family, is any business of yours,' he drawled coolly.

'Oh, dear—it looks as if I might be guilty of bad manners, doesn't it?' She gave him a false, penitent smile.
'I should have enquired after your mother. Tell me—
how *is* dear Eleanor these days? Still busy raising funds
for charity?'

There was a long silence as Leo stared intently at the
calm, self-assured figure smiling so confidently at him
from the other side of his desk. He was damned certain
that he'd never seen this extraordinarily good-looking
girl before. But, if so, how come she seemed to know
his mother?

'And how is your stepfather?' Alex asked brightly.

'I really don't think—'

'It's a long time ago, of course, but I have very fond
memories of Sir Geoffrey—far and away the nicest
member of your family.'

She smiled artlessly at the man whose face had suddenly become a blank mask. Only the piercingly sharp
green eyes gazing at her with hard, intense speculation
gave any hint of the furious mental activity going on
behind that deadpan expression.

'I do hope that he's enjoying his retirement in
Gloucestershire? It must be such a contrast to all those
years he spent as an ambassador in South America!' she
continued, suddenly recalling one of the snippets of information from the newspaper library commenting on
the successful diplomatic career of Sir Geoffrey Lucas
which she'd briefly had time to look at before driving to
the bank.

This girl is definitely trouble—with a capital T! Leo told himself grimly. Although, quite why he was suddenly so certain of that fact, he had no idea. But he still had no clue as to why she was here. Or what she'd hoped to gain by pretending to be Fiona Bliss...

And leaving aside any speculation about her visit to his office, he had a very strong, uneasy feeling that his life was about to be seriously disturbed. Maybe it was that slight trace of irony in her voice? Or, possibly, the sight of those wide, clear blue eyes regarding him with such a guileless, innocent gaze? Whatever the reason, his instincts were telling him that the sooner he got rid of this Miss Pemberton the better it would be for his peace of mind.

'Well, it's been very interesting meeting you, but I'm afraid that I'm going to have to ask you to leave,' he murmured smoothly. 'Unfortunately, I'm very busy today, and...'

'Yes. I listened to your speech downstairs just now. Very impressive!'

'Thank you,' he murmured through gritted teeth, making a mental note to have a few harsh, sharp words with the bank's chief security officer.

The fact that this girl had managed to gain entrance to the building—let alone being able to wander casually around the offices—was absolutely disgraceful! In fact, now he came to think about it, such a total breach of security could have had dire consequences. He was probably lucky that she wasn't some mad gunman, waving a kalashnikov rifle and demanding the keys to the bank's safe!

With a slight, irritated shake of his dark head, Leo made a determined effort to clear his mind.

Oh, boy—it really *wasn't* his day! First all that business about his 'engagement' to Fiona—and now, seemingly bemused by this unknown girl's bewitching smile, he'd *actually* found himself thinking that some crazy idiot might appear in his office brandishing a gun!

Pull yourself together—get a grip on life! he told himself roughly. So...OK, he was prepared to admit that he found Miss Pemberton very sexually attractive. But so what? He had, after all, known plenty of women who were far more beautiful. And yet...well, most unfortunately, there was no escaping the fact that, while she'd only been in his office for a few minutes, this girl appeared to be having a disastrous effect on his normally level-headed, logical mind!

'I have several calls to make, and then an early luncheon appointment,' he informed her curtly, pulling one of the telephones on his desk towards him. 'So, if you don't mind letting yourself out...?'

'Well, yes, I do—mind, that is. Because I was really hoping that we could have a lovely long talk,' Alex told him with another completely false, beaming smile. 'I mean, we've *so* much news to catch up on, haven't we?' she added, leaning back in her chair. 'For instance, I can't wait to hear all about your romance with Fiona Bliss!'

Leo gave a heavy sigh, before slowly rising to his feet. 'I'm sorry, but I really am very busy. So, unless you leave this office immediately, I shall be forced to call the security guards—and have you thrown out.'

'I don't think I'd like that.'

He gave a short bark of exasperated laughter. 'No, I'm quite sure that you wouldn't,' he agreed grimly, determinedly averting his eyes from her long, slim legs in those sexy black stockings. 'So, why not be a sensible girl and leave quietly while you have the chance to do so?'

'Because we've got some talking to do—that's why,' she retorted, opening her handbag and extracting a white business card, which she placed firmly on the desk in front of him.

'I'm simply not interested...' he snapped, irritably flicking the card away as he lifted the receiver of his phone, angrily punching some numbers on the dial.

'Oh, I think you will be interested,' she countered swiftly, leaning forward and firmly cutting off his call. 'Because, while I use the name of Alex Pemberton for professional reasons, I was actually christened Alexandra Rothstein.

'Not that it really matters,' she continued bleakly as he slowly put down the phone. 'Because, as far as you are concerned, Leo, my real name is *Nemesis*!'

CHAPTER THREE

GAZING up at Leo's tall frame, which had suddenly stiffened, his dark brows drawn together in a frown as he stared down at her, Alex found herself wondering why the name of Nemesis—the mythical Greek goddess of retribution and revenge—should have so suddenly come into her mind.

As he replaced the phone and slowly sank back down into his seat, Alex realised that deep down, within the dark recesses of her subconscious, she must have been waiting for an opportunity to finally confront Leo face to face. Not ever really knowing exactly how, when or where, of course. But now the strong feelings of anger and injustice, which she'd so firmly suppressed for the past eight years, were swiftly rising to the surface and demanding to be heard.

Alexandra Rothstein...? 'Well, well...' Leo murmured, leaning back in his chair, regarding her intently from beneath his heavy lids.

'Surprise, surprise!' Alex murmured, taking the opportunity to steady her nerves as she bent down to retrieve her business card, which he'd so arrogantly flicked down onto the floor by her feet.

'It certainly *is* a surprise to see you again after such a long time,' he agreed slowly. 'Especially since you seemed to have completely dropped out of sight for the past eight years. In fact, I can hardly believe...' He paused, staring at her silently for a moment. 'I take it that you really are "The Bolter"'s daughter?'

Alex gave him a cool smile. 'I'm afraid so.'

'So, what's your mother up to these days?' he enquired sardonically. 'The last I heard of Gina, she'd run away from a rich Italian prince—was he her fifth or sixth husband?—and "bolted" off with a young Argentinian polo player. However, I imagine that she must have married and discarded several more husbands by now.'

'She might well have done so,' Alex agreed stonily. 'Unfortunately, my mother and her husband died in an aeroplane crash some years ago.'

'Oh, Lord—I'm sorry!' Leo exclaimed, grimacing in self-disgust and clearly wishing that he'd kept his mouth shut as he brushed a hand roughly through his dark hair.

Alex shrugged. 'Apparently, it seems the young Argentinian was far more skilled at handling his polo ponies than he was at managing the controls of his private plane.'

'I really am very sorry,' Leo assured her earnestly. 'What I said about your mother was completely uncalled for and desperately unkind. Believe me, I had no intention of...'

'Yes, well, it all happened a long time ago,' she said quickly, determined to avoid a discussion on Gina's obvious defects as a wife and mother.

Besides, it had been a generous and handsome apology from Leo, who certainly had no reason to think well of her mother.

His stepfather, Sir Geoffrey Lucas, had only been Gina's second husband for a very short time. Barely a year after their wedding she'd run off with a French pop star, leaving Sir Geoffrey to subsequently marry Leo's mother, Eleanor Hamilton, then a widow with a young ten-year-old son.

Leo glanced down at his watch. 'I really do have a lunch appointment with some bankers. However, I think our ''family reunion'' calls for a quick gin and tonic—don't you?' he murmured, rising from behind his desk to move lithely across the room. He opened a large bookcase to reveal a well-stocked drinks cabinet, and Alex noted that, while busy mixing her an alcoholic drink, he was pouring himself a large glass of plain water.

Suddenly feeling strangely nervous, Alex quickly reviewed her basic strategy for the forthcoming interview. There had been no reason why it shouldn't work. Back at the newspaper office, she'd been quite certain—provided she could get access to the rotten man—that gaining his co-operation would be a fairly straightforward matter. But now, rising to her feet as he strode back across the thick carpet, she was beginning to have severe doubts about her ability to carry out her plans.

Not only did he appear to be taking her unexpected reappearance in his life far too calmly, but it was also proving difficult to ignore the almost overpowering aura of forceful, aggressive masculinity surrounding the man now standing so close to her. As he placed the heavy crystal glass in her hand she almost jumped at the light touch of his fingers, which seemed to send a quick electric shock tingling through her body.

'Well...' Leo drawled reflectively, seating himself casually on the edge of the desk beside her. 'I must say that you've certainly changed since the last time we met. A real case of an ugly duckling changing into an outstandingly beautiful swan.'

'That's nice of you to say so,' she murmured with a cool smile, determinedly blanking out from her mind all memories of their last disastrous encounter. 'But it has been eight years since that summer holiday in Tuscany.' She gave a careless shrug. 'And I was very young at the time.'

'Yes,' he agreed quietly, the heavy lids over his eyes hiding all expression as he rose from the desk and walked slowly over to gaze out of the window.

'However, to be quite frank, Alex,' he continued with a smile as he turned around to face her, 'I have to confess that I'd never have recognised you. Not in a million years.'

'I think I'd have probably shot myself if you had!'

Quite without thought, she found herself grinning in response to the note of warm, sensual amusement in the low rumble of laughter with which he greeted her quick retort.

Swiftly pulling herself together, she buried her nose in the glass, attempting to concentrate on the matter at hand.

She must forget the past. Ignore everything else but the job in hand. Because if she didn't get Leo's co-operation it looked as if she would be waving goodbye to a promising career. And, while he and his family might have ruined her life at the tender age of sixteen, she sure as heck wasn't going to allow herself to be stitched up ever again.

'Well, that was all a long time ago,' she told him with a deliberately nonchalant shrug. 'I'm far more interested in the present. Which reminds me,' she added casually, 'I haven't yet told you why I'm here, have I?'

'Quite right—you haven't,' he agreed dryly, slowly

sipping his glass of water as he gazed reflectively at the girl beside him. 'I wonder why I should have such a strong, instinctive feeling that I don't actually want to know why you've suddenly appeared in my office...?'

The cool, sardonic smile accompanying his words brought a hot flush of colour to her cheeks. Was this damn man clairvoyant—or what? As she saw Leo glance down once again at his watch, Alex realised that she couldn't afford to waste any time exchanging idle chit-chat. Raising her glass to her lips, she took a deep slug of Dutch courage, before placing the heavy tumbler down on his desk.

'You will undoubtedly be relieved to know that I haven't come here to reminisce about the past,' she said. 'Nor do I want a job in this bank, nor to borrow any money.'

'I should think not!' He gave a short bark of sarcastic laughter. 'If I remember rightly, when Gina's mother died you inherited the whole of the Rothstein fortune. Which must mean, my dear Alex, that you're a *very* wealthy young girl. In fact,' he added with a cynical grin, 'it's far more likely that this bank would want to borrow funds from *you.*'

'I was merely making the point that I didn't come here to talk about finance,' she muttered crossly. 'In fact, I'm far more interested in hearing all about your engagement to Fiona Bliss.'

'Oh, really...?' he murmured, his lips twitching as if enjoying a private joke. 'I wonder why?'

'That's why,' she retorted curtly, handing him her card. 'And kindly don't throw it on the floor this time.'

'Well, well...!' he drawled, after swiftly scanning the small white card in his hand. 'Who would have guessed that tiresome little girl, Alexandra Rothstein, would eventually grow up to become beautiful Ms Alex Pemberton, who apparently works for the *London Chronicle*? Incidentally,. why the change of name? Are you now a married woman?'

'Certainly not!' she snapped, before quickly deciding to try to remain as calm as possible for the next few minutes. Especially since it was more than likely that Leo would soon become very angry indeed.

'You may have forgotten that my father, Johnny Pemberton—the international racing driver—was Gina's first husband,' she explained. 'He was killed in a race just before I was born. So, although Gina dumped me on her mother when I was only a few weeks old, and my grandmother subsequently had me christened as Alexandra Rothstein, I'm really—'

'Thank you!' Leo drawled scathingly. 'I think we can do without a long discussion of your family tree.' He put down his glass on the desk. 'So, what are you trying to tell me? That you're the editor's secretary?'

'Isn't that just *typical*?' she exclaimed in disgust. 'Why do so many men automatically assume that a woman is only capable of being a glorified typist?'

'Oops—sorry!' His lips twitched with amusement. 'I can't seem to keep up with all the politically correct titles these days. Would calling you a ''personal assistant'' be more acceptable? After all, no one's likely to believe that you're some kind of reporter,' he added with a condescending smile, which she found deeply irritating.

'Oh, really…? Why not?'

Leo shrugged, his green eyes glinting with suppressed laughter as they roamed over her figure. 'My dear girl,' he drawled. 'You don't exactly look like a representative of the gutter press! Certainly not those I've had the misfortune to meet.'

'Oh, right!' She grinned maliciously up at him. 'You mean that because I'm not wearing a grubby raincoat, lurking in a doorway, or brandishing a notebook and tape recorder I can't possibly be a reporter?'

'Well…'

'Get a life, Leo!' she exclaimed with a snort of derision. 'You may find it difficult to believe—especially working in an ancient time capsule like this old Victorian building—but we *are* just about to hit the twenty-first century. In recent times there have been at least two female editors of national newspapers. And believe me,' Alex added with a grim laugh, 'neither of them would have been seen *dead* in a grubby old raincoat!'

'Are you trying to tell me that you really are a genuine, bona fide journalist?'

'*Ding dong!* Give the man a prize for coming up with the right answer—at last!' she drawled in a close imitation of his own scathing tone of voice as she opened her handbag to show him her press card.

There was a long silence following her words. All trace of amusement had been wiped from his face, which now looked as if it was carved from a piece of cold marble; his hard green eyes stared at her with a grim, deep intensity she found distinctly unnerving. It felt as if he was trying to mentally bore his way into her head, the tension mounting second by second until Alex could almost feel it thudding like a sledge-hammer against her skull.

She had no idea how long they'd been locked in mental conflict when the spell was finally broken by the harsh sound of Leo swearing violently beneath his breath. Swiftly rising from his perch on the edge of his desk, he strode across the room towards the drinks cupboard.

'It's obviously time I had a stiff drink,' he rasped harshly, slowly turning around to face her. 'Well, Alex, it seems that I've been guilty of making a serious error. Because it's now clear that this is very far from being just a friendly family visit. Right?'

'Oh, come on!' She gave him a cold, wintry smile. 'Both you and your parents have happily ignored my existence for the past eight years. So where you got the idea that I came here to your office simply to play a game of Happy Families, I've no idea.'

'Is this some sort of crazy revenge for what happened all those years ago?' he demanded incredulously.

'No, of course it isn't,' she assured him swiftly, suddenly startled to discover that she was, in fact, almost telling the truth.

She did, naturally, still feel a hard lump of resentment over the way his family had treated her. But, having at last forced herself to confront Leo, it all now seemed relatively unimportant, somehow. She was no longer that unhappy, gauche teenager, terrified of saying or doing the wrong thing in public and almost dying from embarrassment and shame at his family's reaction to her weird appearance.

'I've come here to see you today because I need your help,' she told him firmly. 'To be honest, I don't have happy memories of that summer holiday eight years ago. But I'd like to believe that we can forget what happened in the past. I was delighted to hear about your engage-

ment, and I sincerely hope that you and Fiona will be
very happy together.'

He gazed at her stony-faced for a moment, before
shrugging his broad shoulders and strolling across the
thick pile carpet to the fireplace.

'Thank you for your...er...good wishes,' he murmured smoothly, leaning casually against the mantelpiece. 'And, of course, you're quite right. It's always
pointless to look back at the past. However much one
might wish to rectify matters, there's no going back, is
there?'

And that, Alex told herself grimly, is all the apology
you're ever likely to get!

'I think you mentioned that you needed my help,' Leo
was saying. 'What's the problem?'

'It isn't exactly a problem, as such. More the fact that
I need your assistance with two feature articles I'm writing for my newspaper.'

He frowned. 'I've never thought of the *Chronicle* as
a paper particularly interested in financial affairs.
However,' he added with a shrug, 'I'll certainly do what
I can to assist you.'

'Well...I'm not actually writing about finance,' she
told him, before taking a deep breath and explaining
exactly why she needed his co-operation.

'There's no need to worry about the style or content
of the articles,' she concluded nervously in the heavy,
ominous silence which had greeted her explanation. Leo
continued to regard her with a totally blank expression
on his tanned face. 'It may be immodest to say so, but
I *am* a good writer. And I intend to concentrate far more
on the traditional class aspects of an engagement rather
than the various personalities concerned. Besides which,'

she added quickly, 'don't forget that there are two other couples involved. So, only a third of the article will be about you and Fiona.'

'Is that it?' he queried blandly as she finally came to a halt.

'Er...yes, I think I've just about covered everything.'

'You certainly have!' he muttered in a strangled voice.

A brief second later, to her complete astonishment, she saw him throw back his dark head and give a great bellow of laughter. 'Oh, Lord!' he groaned, clutching the mantelpiece for support as his tall body was shaken by heavy gusts of mirth. 'I haven't had such a good laugh in years!'

'I'm glad you think it's so funny,' she snapped.

'F-funny...?' he gasped, producing a large white linen handkerchief and wiping the tears of laughter from his eyes. 'Never make the mistake of under-selling yourself, Alex. Believe me—the whole idea of such a crazy project is totally *hilarious*!'

'So, I can count on both your and Fiona's help?' she asked, almost unable to believe that it had been so easy to gain his help and co-operation.

'Don't be ridiculous!' he retorted, the laughter draining swiftly from his face. 'Goodness knows, I like a good joke. But if you seriously think that I, or my...er...fiancée, would have anything to do with that ghastly, down-market rag you work for—let alone co-operate with what sounds like a thoroughly nauseating and obnoxious article—you must be out of your tiny mind!'

'Oh, come on, Leo. I really *do* need your help,' she begged.

'Forget it!' he snapped curtly, before glancing once

more down at the thin gold watch on his wrist. 'If I don't get a move on, I'm going to be late for my lunch appointment. It's definitely been interesting to meet you again,' he added, walking towards his desk. 'Maybe we can get together some other time?'

Alex gave a heavy sigh at his brisk dismissal. 'I hope you're going to remember that I did at least try to ask you nicely.'

'Hmm...?' he muttered, clearly absorbed by his business affairs as he checked through some files in his briefcase.

Gazing at his dark head as he concentrated on the papers in front of him, she took a deep breath and tried to summon up all her courage. What she was going to have to do next was nothing less than a crude blackmail attempt in order to force Leo's hand.

She could never, of course, actually bring herself to carry out such a dreadful course of action. However, it was desperately important that he should believe her capable of doing such an awful thing. So why she should suddenly find herself hoping that he *wouldn't* believe her, she had absolutely no idea.

'Are you still here?' He raised his head to gaze at her with an irritated frown.

'I can't go yet, I'm afraid. Not until we've sorted this matter out.'

'Really, Alex!' he groaned in exasperation, shaking his dark head as he leaned back in his chair. 'You can't have seriously imagined that I'd agree to your crazy scheme? Why on earth would I want to have details of my private life splattered all over the gutter press? There is such a thing as a right to privacy, you know.'

'Yes, I know. And I really wouldn't do this to you,

Leo—not if my career wasn't at stake,' she assured him earnestly. 'However, I reckon that after what happened to me in Italy you and your family owe me something. And I'm now here to collect the payment due.'

'The cost is too high,' he snapped, before giving a stiff, uncomfortable shrug of his shoulders. 'While I am prepared to agree that you were, indeed, treated in a shameful manner, there's no way I'd ever agree to help you with your article.'

'And you won't change your mind?'

'I'm sorry, Alex, but that is *definitely* my last word on the subject,' he agreed grimly.

'Well, I'm sorry, too.' She shrugged. 'Because, if my career is about to go down the tubes, I'm going to have to take you and your mother down with me.'

'What…?'

'Providing it's a human interest story, a journalist is in a prime position to have an article printed in his or her own newspaper,' she told him quietly, keeping a wary eye on his suddenly rigid figure as she strolled about the room. 'And if you can add some tear-jerking aspects to the story, it can often be a real winner.'

'So…?' he growled.

'So… I was thinking of writing a piece for the *Chronicle*'s "true-life story" page. It concerns a young girl whose father died before she was born and who was subsequently abandoned by her foolish, socialite mother. Raised in lonely isolation by her rich grandmother—who died when the girl wasn't quite sixteen—she found herself completely alone in the world, with no one to give a toss what happened to her. Other than her trustees, of course.

'But they were far too busy—looking after the huge

amount of money she'd been left in her grandmother's will—to care one way or another about the girl,' Alex added with a brief, cynical laugh. 'It's a sad story, isn't it?'

'Yes,' he agreed slowly, his brows drawn together in a deep frown.

'Things could have been far worse, of course,' she continued briskly. 'Our young heroine certainly wasn't either poor, homeless or the victim of abuse. Just damn lonely. So, imagine the nervous mixture of excitement and dread when she heard that one of her mother's many ex-husbands—an ambassador, no less!—had offered to have her to stay at his holiday home in Italy for the long summer vacation. Unfortunately, I have to admit that the silly girl had become a bit bolshie by this time. And, in a foolish spirit of rebellion against an unkind world, she'd succeeded in making herself look spectacularly ugly.

'Still, she *was* very young,' Alex added reflectively. 'So you'd expect grown up, sophisticated people—such as the ambassador's current wife, and her glamorous twenty-three year-old son—to be understanding, even if they didn't approve of her appearance. But, no! It was definitely a case of shock, horror and dismay all round. Even her stepbrother—for whom our heroine had, of course, developed an intense if fleeting teenage passion—spent a good deal of his time making fun of her to his friends.'

'That's a damned lie!' Leo ground out. 'I'm sorry if you felt we were making fun of you—but your paranoia is hardly my fault. Besides,' he added angrily, 'I was seven years older than you. Why would I bother to take any notice of a young teenager?'

There was a long silence following his last words, which hung heavily in the air between them as they stared grimly at one another.

Just about to open her mouth and remind him of the time when he *had* taken notice of her, Alex felt her courage fail her at the last minute. She simply couldn't bear to go through the whole hideous scene, which she'd spent so many years trying to forget. And, from the slight flush colouring his cheekbones, the muscle beating wildly in his jaw as he carefully avoided her gaze, it seemed as if Leo, too, would prefer not to recall the past.

'Um…well, to continue…' Alex muttered. 'Where was I? Oh, yes…now we come to the really, *really* sad part of the story. Because while her husband, the ambassador, was away for a few days, our heroine's stepmother suddenly took leave of her senses. Accusing the girl of stealing a valuable diamond brooch, which had unaccountably gone missing, she went completely bananas—and called in the local police.

'Luckily, our heroine only spent a few hours in the local damp, evil-looking jail before the stupid woman found the brooch where she'd left it—on a small shelf in the bathroom,' Alex ground out angrily. 'But can you imagine the trauma of the poor young girl, who *knew* she was innocent? Or the terrifying nightmares which plagued her for years after the event? And—almost the worst crime of all—*never* receiving even the slightest apology from the stepmother, who quickly bundled the girl back to England, as if wishing to get rid of a bad smell.'

'*Please, Alex!* Surely there's no need to put yourself through all this yet again?' he protested, obviously very uncomfortable at being reminded of his family's treatment of the girl.

'Actually, I think I'm going to feel a whole lot better once I've put it all down on paper.' She gave a weary shrug of her slim shoulders.

'But...but surely you must remember that as soon as I returned to the villa I got you out of jail as fast as possible?'

'That still doesn't excuse what happened, does it?' she pointed out grimly.

There was a long pause, finally broken as Leo gave a heavy sigh, brushing a hand roughly through his dark hair. 'I have no excuse to offer for my mother's behaviour,' he acknowledged tersely. 'You...you must know how deeply I regret what happened.'

'I do recall a very reluctant, stiff apology from you at the time. But that wasn't likely to be much comfort to me, was it?'

'Stiff?' he growled. 'That's rich! You were as spiky as a hedgehog.'

'How in hell did you expect me to act, after such an experience? No wonder I went completely to pieces later that evening!' Alex retorted angrily, spinning around to face him and noting, once again, that he wasn't quite able to look her straight in the eye. As if he, too, was reluctant to recall the events of that hot, stifling night in Tuscany.

'It's clearly *not* an edifying story,' she continued grimly. 'And I don't suppose your mother will be too thrilled to see her name in print. Especially as I understand that she's organising a charity ball next week. Still, maybe some of her good friends will stand by her. What do you think?'

'What do I think...?' he echoed, staring at her in horror. 'For God's sake, Alex—you simply can't *do* this!'

'Oh, yes, I can...and I will.'

'Not while I've got breath in my body!' His harshly voiced savage response cracked across the room like a whiplash as he rose swiftly from his seat, striding rapidly across the carpet towards her.

'Now, keep calm, Leo...' she muttered, backing nervously away from the rigidly angry figure bearing down upon her. 'There's no need to lose your rag like this.'

'Oh, no?' he exploded as she felt her spine jar up against the marble mantelpiece. 'I don't care about myself. But, if you think that I'm going to allow some... some *cheapjack journalist* to ruin my mother's life, you've got another think coming!' he added with a grim snarl, firmly grasping hold of her arm.

Alex glared up at the rigidly angry expression on his face, only too well aware of her nervous, erratic heartbeat at the close proximity of the man looming so threateningly over her.

'Take your hands off me,' she cried out, struggling to break free of his iron grip.

'Believe me—I'd be more than happy to place them *very* tightly around your throat!' he ground out menacingly through clenched teeth, swiftly pulling her wriggling figure firmly up against his hard, masculine body.

His action having momentarily left her gasping for breath, Alex found herself staring up at his face, now only inches away from her own.

'Can't you see that what you're intending to do is totally and utterly despicable?' he demanded bitterly.

'Yes...' she whispered helplessly, mesmerised by the cruel glint in the angry green eyes glaring furiously down at her. 'I know that it's a really awful thing to do, but...' Her voice died away as she found herself unable to tear her gaze from his.

As they stood locked together in a strange silence, broken only by the distant rumble of City traffic and the faint hiss of the gas-fuelled log fire behind her, the expression in his eyes seemed to change. Slowly growing dark and opaque, they conveyed a message which triggered a subconscious response deep in her body. Suddenly it felt as if the blood was pounding in her head, her heart racing like a metronome out of control as his arms slowly tightened like bands of steel about her slim, trembling figure.

Even through the thickness of their respective clothing she could feel the increasingly rapid thud of his heart, echoing her own wild pulse-beats; her nostrils filled with the warm, musky scent of his cologne and her body was suddenly shockingly aware of his own arousal as his dark head came down towards her.

Much later, when she tried to come to grips with what had happened in Leo's office, Alex would be completely at a loss to account for her own quite extraordinary behaviour.

After all, it wasn't as if she was a nervous virgin, afraid to say boo to a goose. She was twenty-four years of age, and well able to look after herself, right? So, why hadn't she shouted and screamed blue murder? Or, at the very least, made a serious attempt to struggle and fight her way free of the foul man's embrace?

Unfortunately, the only conclusion she would come to would be that she must have been struck down by a total mental paralysis! Nothing else could satisfactorily explain why, instead of a vigorous protest, she so swiftly became oblivious to everything except the fierce, over-powering rush of excitement which scorched through her body as his hard, firm mouth possessed hers.

For a few, mad moments she abandoned herself to the overpowering intoxication of his kiss, her lips parting breathlessly beneath the ruthless savagery and determination of his lips and tongue. And then, as the warning sirens began wailing loudly in her fuddled mind, she at last made a feeble attempt to struggle free of his arms. Only to find that she'd left it far too late; his hand swept up to hold her head firmly and immovably beneath his own.

Her traitorous body seemed determined to ignore the danger signals flashing so loudly in her brain, instinctively melting against his hard, firm chest as her arms wound themselves up about his neck. There was no resistance from her as his hands moved caressingly down over her soft curves. Her senses apparently drugged and seduced into quivering acquiescence as his experienced fingers rapidly undid the buttons of her close-fitting jacket, they allowed his lips passage down over her throat and neck, to search for the warm swell of her breasts.

Goodness knows what might have happened next, had they not been interrupted by the sudden appearance of Leo's personal assistant.

One moment it seemed as though she was drowning in ecstasy, and the next she found herself being pushed abruptly away, her ears filled with the sound of Leo cursing violently under his breath.

'Excuse me, Mr Hamilton...so sorry...I thought you'd already left for your lunch appointment...' Dora muttered incoherently, her cheeks flushing a bright crimson as she hurriedly turned to leave the room.

'Make my excuses about lunch. Say that I've been unavoidably detained, but will join them for coffee later,' Leo barked over his shoulder, his tall body shielding Alex's dazed, trembling and dishevelled figure from his assistant's sight until he heard the sound of the door closing firmly behind her.

In the ghastly silence that followed Dora's departure, Alex could only lean helplessly against the marble mantelpiece, frantically trying to do up the buttons of her jacket with fingers which seemed to be made of cotton wool.

Eventually summoning up enough nerve to peek cautiously through her eyelashes at Leo, she saw that he was gazing down at her with stunned eyes, as if staring at a ghost, his face pale beneath its tan. However, as their eyes met, he turned abruptly on his heel, marching back across the thick carpet to sit down at his desk.

Leaning back in his chair, he appeared buried in deep thought for some moments, before giving a heavy sigh.

'You'd better come and sit down,' he rasped harshly. 'What happened, just now...' He shrugged his broad shoulders. 'There's obviously no point in trying to explain the inexplicable—so I'm not even going to try. I suggest that we both do our best to forget the last five minutes.'

Miserably aware that she had just made an almighty fool of herself, Alex could only give a helpless nod of agreement. Stumbling across the room on legs which felt as though they were made of jelly, she sank thankfully down onto the chair in front of his desk.

'Well, Alex, we clearly have a problem,' he said at

last. 'If I understand the situation correctly, it seems that, unless I agree to allow you to write an article about myself and my fiancée, you have every intention of exposing my mother's extremely stupid, unkind behaviour in the past. Correct?'

'Um…yes, I suppose so,' she muttered, unable to meet his eyes as she stared unhappily down at the clenched hands in her lap.

'Tell me,' he drawled scathingly, 'do you usually blackmail your victims in pursuit of a story?'

'No, of course I don't!' she retorted angrily, raising her head to glare at the handsome, stern features of the man sitting across the desk. 'I can promise you that I've never done anything like this in my life before.'

'Which is hardly an excuse for doing it now.'

'OK…OK,' she mumbled, brushing a shaking hand through her hair. 'If it's any consolation, I'm thoroughly ashamed of having to bring this sort of pressure to bear. And I wouldn't be doing so if I wasn't absolutely desperate,' she confessed with a heavy sigh.

'Desperate…?'

She shrugged. 'The truth is, Leo, that if I don't get this story I'm going to lose my job.'

'All the more reason to have you thrown out of this office *toute de suite!*' he retorted with a grim bark of laughter.

'Ha, ha!' she ground out sarcastically, deciding that she'd *never* hated anyone as much as she did this foul man. 'Anyway, that's the only reason why I'm here,' she added bitterly. 'Why else would I want to have anything to do with you—or your rotten family?'

There was another long, heavy silence as he stared at

the flushed cheeks and unhappy blue eyes of the girl
sitting across the desk.

'Very well,' he said at last in a hard, grating voice.
'Despite your attempt at blackmail, I don't actually happen to believe that you would have written an article
about my mother. In fact, I'm very sure that you've been
using the possibility of doing so merely as a threat to
gain my co-operation. However, that's clearly not a risk
I can take.'

'Do you mean...? Are you really going to help me?'
she gasped, almost overcome with relief.

'I wouldn't get too excited, if I were you,' he retorted
grimly. 'You haven't yet heard my terms for going along
with this totally mad project. For one thing, I'm going
to insist that you will not—under any circumstances—
try to make contact with my mother.'

'I'm hardly likely to do that,' Alex pointed out coldly.
'In fact, she's just about the very *last* person I'd want
to see.'

He sighed. 'Yes, well...there's no doubt that she
treated you very badly in the past. While it's probably
no excuse, I can tell you that it seems she was suffering
from a bad hormonal imbalance and acute depression at
the time.'

'I'm sorry to hear that,' Alex told him stiffly, still
unwilling to forgive or forget the older woman's cruel
behaviour.

'I'm also going to insist on having full control of what
you write,' he continued grimly. 'And that means that
nothing—*absolutely nothing*—gets published unless and
until I've read and approved of every damn word!'

'No problem. That's fine by me,' she assured him
quickly, realising that she would, of course, face a battle

with her editor about the fact that Leo was going to be claiming censorship. But she'd cross that bridge when she came to it.

'Anything else?'

'No, not at the moment. I'm flying to Frankfurt this evening, for a brief conference with our new German partners. So this rubbish of yours will have to be put on hold, until my return.' He glanced impatiently down at his watch, before adding bleakly, 'I suggest that, under the circumstances, you'd better leave here as quickly as you can—before I change my mind.'

His mouth firmed into a thin, hard line, his green eyes glinting with suppressed fury at having being outwitted by this chit of a girl, now rising to her feet and smiling brightly down at him as if she hadn't a care in the world.

Well...if Ms Alexandra Pemberton thought that she was going to get the better of him, she was in for a rude awakening. Because he was definitely going to find a way to make this...this brazen hussy very sorry that she'd ever had the sheer gall and bare-faced downright impertinence to try and twist his arm like this. *Very sorry indeed!*

CHAPTER FOUR

FORCING her way through the noisy crowd of people milling around the bar, Alex spotted the dark head of her friend Sophie, who was seated at a corner table on the far side of the large room.

'I'm sorry to be so late,' she called out, squeezing past a fat, red-faced man before sitting down on the lumpy red leather bench seat beside her friend.

'I hope you realise that you're paying for this pub lunch,' Sophie muttered, clearly still in a bad mood as she waved her hand at the pile of empty plates on the table in front of her.

'No problem,' Alex assured her. 'Did you manage to get hold of the information I wanted?'

'Of course I did! Why do you think I've have been comfort-eating like this?' the other girl retorted belligerently.

Alex laughed. 'Oh, come on! It can't have been as bad as all that.'

'A fat lot you know,' her friend grumbled. 'I've never been so frightened in all my life. It might be all in a day's work for you investigative journalists—but I'm hardly one of life's natural burglars. Right?'

'I know I shouldn't have asked you, but…'

'There's no "but" about it!' Sophie pointed out grimly. 'Our magazine may only deal with the fripperies of life, like reporting fashion trends and high life in society. But, if anyone discovers that I've raided the office files, there's likely to be hell to pay. In fact,' she added gloomily, 'it would probably end up with me losing my job.'

'I'm quite certain it won't ever come to that. And I really am *very* grateful for your help,' Alex murmured soothingly, turning to smile up at a waiter as he placed a clean glass on the table. 'What did you manage to find out about Fiona Bliss and her family?'

Sophie gave a heavy sigh, waiting until the waiter had moved away before glancing furtively around the crowded room as she handed over a plastic bag. 'I took copies of everything that I could lay hands on.'

'Great!'

'I wouldn't get too excited.' Her friend gave a grim snort of laughter. 'That information is going to cost you an arm and a leg. Because, after what I went through today, my price is now the use of your *whole* wardrobe for the foreseeable future.'

'OK…OK.' Alex grinned as she lifted her hands in mock surrender. 'So, what did you find out?'

'Well…basically it seems that George Bliss comes from Newcastle, and is a no-nonsense, hard-working sort of guy. Apparently, he became a multi-*multi*-millionaire on the sale of his margarine business to a large international company. Obviously flush with money, he then bought a large estate in Hampshire.

'George appears to be a nice man. He's a bit of a rough diamond, of course,' Sophie added reflectively. 'But he's apparently developed a keen interest in conservation of the English countryside, and gets on well with his new neighbours. In the meantime, his wife, Ethel—who, by the way, sounds a really *ghastly* woman!—has concentrated on spending their newly acquired wealth, mostly in a determined effort to launch herself, and her daughter, into high society.'

'Has she been successful?'

Sophie poured some wine into her friend's glass, and topped up her own.

'Well…if throwing money around like it's going out of fashion, getting yourself onto a lot of charity ball committees, and being photographed at all the right parties is what turns you on, then I reckon Ethel Bliss isn't doing too badly. As far as I can make out, she seems to be a pushy, tough old bird, with the hide of a rhinoceros, who rules her family with a rod of iron.'

'What about the daughter?'

'As you'll see from the stuff I've given you, there isn't much there about Fiona Bliss. She does occasional part-time work in an old schoolfriend's boutique in Chelsea, is apparently supposed to be mad on horses, and spends as much time as possible at the family home in the country.'

'But what's she like?' Alex probed.

'I've never met the girl. So, how the heck would I know?' Sophie shrugged. 'If her photographs are anything to go by, she's obviously very pretty. And that has to be a real bonus, as far as her formidable mother is concerned. Because, according to the gossip in our office this morning, finding an upper class and well-connected husband for her daughter seems to have been Ethel's top priority.'

'You're right. Ethel Bliss sounds awful!' Alex muttered with a grimace.

'With a mother like that—who needs enemies?' her friend agreed. 'By the way—is that newspaper report

true? Has Fiona really managed to land Leo
Hamilton…?'

'It certainly looks like it,' Alex said. 'I'm going to be
featuring their romance, as well as one or two other couples', in our St Valentine's Day issue. Which was why
I needed that information so badly,' she added, quickly
deciding *not* to tell her old friend about her meeting with
Leo in his office earlier that day.

'Wow—I can't wait to read all about it!' Sophie
laughed. 'I mean…have Fiona and her mother now got
a tiger by the tail, or what? You should see *his* file. I
reckon he must have romanced just about every good-
looking woman in London!'

'So I hear,' Alex murmured, concentrating on eating
the sandwich Sophie had saved her, and hoping that the
dim lighting in their dark corner of the room would prevent the sudden sweep of hot colour she could feel rising
over her cheeks from becoming too obvious.

Unfortunately, she had no excuse for her behaviour in
Leo's office. Especially not after hearing from James
Boswell, at the editorial conference this morning, all
about Leo's lethal reputation with women. So, how
could she have allowed the rotten man to kiss her? And,
what was even worse, *why* hadn't she screamed, or
kicked his shins, or…or at least made *some* effort to
extricate herself from his embrace? Unfortunately, try as
she might, Alex could think of no sane, logical reason
for having completely lost her marbles.

And the questions were still buzzing like angry bees
in her tired brain the next afternoon as she drove down
the motorway to interview Fiona Bliss.

After her late lunch with Sophie, yesterday, she'd hurried home to pore over the press cuttings provided by

her friend, and to tell Dave Morris about the proposed
St Valentine's Day Ball.

Dave, and his girlfriend Kelly, were the people she'd
chosen to represent the 'working-class couple' for her
article. Although, as she'd quickly reminded herself
when typing up her notes late last night, the old class
structures didn't really apply nowadays. Because
Dave—a self-employed plumber—earned considerably
more money each year than Nigel, her 'middle-class' tax
inspector.

She'd first come across Dave a month ago, when the
tank in her roof had sprung a leak following a hard frost
and she'd had water pouring down into her bedroom.
Having mended the tank, Dave had cast a jaundiced eye
over her central heating system.

'You won't get through the winter with that boiler.
And I wouldn't fancy *my* chances with all that antiquated
pipe-work, neither!' he'd announced in a voice heavy
with doom. Which had resulted in Alex employing him
to put in a new, modern system—and to Dave becoming
virtually a member of her household for the past month.

Their friendship, forged over numerous cups of sweet
tea—the fuel apparently required to keep Dave working
at full pitch—had led to her hearing all about his relationship with Kelly, who ran her own hairdressing salon,
and their plans to get engaged on St Valentine's day.
Since it was their romance which had first given her the
idea, Alex had been pleased when the couple had agreed
to feature in the article she was writing for the
Chronicle. And highly relieved when Dave, on hearing
about attending the ball, had merely grinned and said, 'I
reckon it sounds like a good laugh.'

Trying to find the perfect middle-class couple had

proved a difficult problem—one that had only been solved when Dave had suggested his own local tax inspector.

'Nigel's all right,' he'd assured Alex. 'A bit uptight, of course. Nobody likes to think that they're known as public enemy number one, right? But my Kelly does his girlfriend's hair, and we've got sort of friendly with both Susan and Nigel. Well…as friendly as you *can* get with a guy who believes that just about *everyone* tries to cheat the tax man. And he's not far wrong!' Dave had added with a knowing grin.

When she'd finally met them, Nigel Adams and his fiancée, Susan, had proved to be a bright and happy couple, both very keen on sport of all kinds and spending a lot of time at the local gym, keeping fit. Nigel had been a bit hesitant about the article, but Susan's mother— clearly a determined, forceful lady—had been over the moon about the idea of *her* daughter's engagement appearing in a newspaper.

After phoning the lady last night—principally to make arrangements about Susan and Nigel's attendance at the St Valentine's Day Ball—Alex had come to the conclusion that Susan's tough, formidable mother sounded like a sister under the skin to Ethel Bliss!

So, it's two down—and just one to go, Alex told herself now, as she pulled into a parking lay-by, checking the map for the correct route to her destination.

Never having visited this part of the country, she wanted to make sure that she took the right turning off the motorway. She'd already wasted quite enough time trying to track down Fiona Bliss in London. And it looked as if this trip down to Hampshire was likely to be her only chance of getting to meet the girl on her own—without Leo.

'He never actually told me that I *wasn't* allowed to interview his fiancée,' she said aloud, trying to sound a lot more brave and confident than she felt. Because it was no good trying to fool herself. She knew very well that Leo would be absolutely *furious* when he learned what she'd been up to.

Well...that's just too bad! she thought defiantly. He shouldn't have let drop the fact that he was going to be out of the country. It was, after all, asking too much to expect her to forgo the opportunity of having a proper, in-depth, 'all girls together' type of interview with Fiona. Something that would be quite impossible with her fiancé present.

Besides, Leo had made it very clear that he loathed the whole idea of her article. He was obviously going to do all he could to avoid going through with their agreement. Making sure that Fiona was kept under wraps and well away from the 'gutter press' was an obvious way of torpedoing the feature, and making it very difficult for Alex to write anything worth reading.

However, she hadn't worked on newspapers for the past four years without learning how to cope with such problems. Leo might think he was a really smart, clever guy. But, if he thought she was going to allow herself to be out-manoeuvred, he was in for a big surprise, Alex told herself grimly as she started up her car and pulled out into the traffic.

In the past, he'd been the one holding all the cards. So it was going to give her great pleasure to turn the tables on the foul man. That would teach him, she told herself viciously, before a quotation she'd come across recently suddenly popped into her head. Who was it that had said, 'Always be civil to the girls, you never know who they may marry'...? Or—more accurately in her case—what *job* they might end up with! So, maybe by the time she'd finished with Leo, the next time he had any dealings with a young, vulnerable teenager he might take care not to be quite so ruthlessly cruel and dismissive.

As the traffic ground to a slow crawl, due to lane closures for some roadworks, Alex leaned back in her seat and gave a heavy sigh.

If only she hadn't been such an idiot! If she hadn't been urged on by her stupid pride—and an equally foolish determination to score off Imogen Hall-Knightly—she wouldn't be rushing around the country, trying to make good her promise that she *could*, and *would*, produce the St Valentine's Day article. Nor would she have been forced to face those ghosts which she had spent so many years trying to forget.

Instead of which—thanks to her own stupidity—her job was now firmly on the line. And, even worse, ever since she'd seen that piece of gossip about Leo's engagement, her mind had been almost permanently swamped by unhappy memories of the past...

While it might be unfair to blame her mother, there was no doubt that it was one of Gina Rothstein's many disastrous marriages which had led to so much trouble for her daughter.

Alex often wondered if her supremely selfish mother had ever known, or cared, about the problems which she'd caused so many people before her own life had been abruptly terminated by that plane crash in Mexico. Piloted by her sixth husband, a rich young Argentinian polo player, the fatal accident had finally brought to an end Gina's marital escapades, which had led to her nickname, 'The Bolter'.

There was no reason why Gina Rothstein, a much cherished only child born late to immensely wealthy parents, should have turned out to be so wild. Extraordinarily beautiful, she had been expected to make a glittering marriage. But, headstrong and well out of control by the age of seventeen, Gina had run away from home to enjoy a rip-roaring, very public love affair with Johnny Pemberton—an equally wild, wealthy young racing driver.

Johnny's death in a race at Nuremberg had left Gina both inconsolable for a time—and pregnant. However, clearly not having a maternal bone in her lovely body, Gina had soon dumped the newborn baby girl on her mother, and swiftly 'bolted' once more to join the jet set, subsequently marrying and discarding a whole string of husbands.

Alex smiled as she fondly recalled the small, upright and imperious figure of her grandmother, whose heart of true gold had been buried deep beneath a very stern exterior. A widow and, at sixty years of age, not exactly a spring chicken, she had nevertheless brought up the little girl—whom she'd christened Alexandra Rothstein—as carefully and strictly as if she'd been her own child.

Lucky to have been raised in a grand mansion, situated deep in the English countryside, Alex now knew that she'd been even more lucky to have had such a happy, secure start in life. And, when she'd been sent to a boarding school at the age of twelve, she'd soon discovered—after listening to the unhappy stories of some of her new friends—that a rich, privileged background meant nothing without the warmth and love of a caring family.

However, all good things must come to an end. And they had ended abruptly for Alex just before her sixteenth birthday. Only a few days after completing her school exams, she'd learned that her grandmother had suddenly died in her sleep.

Continually 'bolting' from one husband to another, Gina had clearly forgotten all about her young daughter. Which was possibly why their one and only meeting, in the pouring rain at the graveside of Alex's grandmother, had been such a disaster.

'Oh, my God—I simply *don't* believe it!' Gina had exclaimed in horror-struck tones. Her baby-blue eyes widening in disbelief, she had stared up at the thin, gawky teenager who, at a height of five feet ten inches, towered over her own delicate, petite figure. 'There *must* be some mistake. I couldn't *possibly* have given birth to a girl who's as plain as ditch water!'

Still in a complete state of shock and misery, Alex had felt hot tears roll down her face as she gazed bemusedly down at the beautiful, elegant stranger.

'It's just as well that your grandmother left you all her money,' Gina had drawled when the service ended, clearly furious at being cut out of her own mother's will. 'Because, quite frankly, *darling*—with those looks, you're going to need every penny you can lay your hands on!' she'd added spitefully, before turning to the deeply tanned, handsome young husband by her side and demanding to be taken immediately back to London in her chauffeured limousine.

Not only was that the first and last time she'd ever seen her mother, it was also the day that Alex had learned of her huge inheritance. Not that it had meant anything to her at the time, of course. Totally stunned and grief-stricken by the loss of the one person who had ever really cared for her, she'd hardly heard the dry-as-dust tones of the lawyer informing her about the trust fund, which was designed to make sure that she would always be financially secure.

Still mentally frozen with misery, Alex had returned to school, spending the remaining few weeks of the summer term in a complete daze. However, while she was totally listless and apathetic about her future, it seemed that her headmistress and trustees had been active on her behalf.

Realising that Gina was obviously a broken reed, they had contacted the only one of her ex-husbands who could, by any stretch of the imagination, be considered a respectable man. In fact, Sir Geoffrey Lucas, a well-known diplomat at the Foreign Office, had only been briefly married to the beautiful and fascinating Gina, before she'd upped and run away with a French pop star.

However, despite his second happy marriage to a widow—who already had a son, Leo Hamilton, some seven years older than Alex—Sir Geoffrey had kindly offered to look after the orphan girl whom he'd never met, inviting her to spend the summer vacation at his holiday home in Tuscany.

Now, as she looked back at that long, hot summer, Alex could easily understand why Sir Geoffrey's wife, Eleanor, hadn't been at all happy about having a young teenager dumped on her.

'I can't *think* what my husband thought he was doing,' she'd grumbled on Alex's arrival. 'You're far too young to have anything in common with Leo or his friends. So you'll just have to try and amuse yourself. And what on earth possessed you to dye your hair that *frightful* colour is quite beyond me!'

Unfortunately, Alex had been unable to supply a sensible answer. In fact, she'd had no idea why, after that disastrous encounter with Gina at her grandmother's funeral, she'd suddenly decided to embrace the Gothic style, as if almost deliberately trying to look as ugly as possible.

'I'm simply not prepared to put up with such a *hideous* sight,' Eleanor Lucas had told her firmly. 'We can't do much about that awful dead-black colour, of course. However, as soon as I can make an appointment, I'm going to insist on taking you to my hairdresser and having it cut off as short as possible. In the meantime, you will kindly keep to your room. I see no reason why my guests should have to set eyes on such a *ghastly* sight.

'There is just one more thing I'd like to say,' Eleanor had continued sternly. 'Whatever else you do, Alexandra, kindly don't make the mistake of falling in love with my son, Leo. Young girls in the throes of unrequited love are *such* a bore,' she'd added with an exasperated sigh. 'And there are far too many silly, empty-headed females mooning around after him as it is!'

But, of course, as Alex now bitterly acknowledged, she'd been a total and utter fool. Because, barely moments after setting eyes on the tall, dark, handsome twenty-three-year-old, she'd forgotten all his mother's really excellent advice…and fallen blindly in love with Leo Hamilton.

The sudden sound of a sharp, angry toot on a horn

from the car behind her suddenly jerked Alex back to
the present.

Clearly, while she'd been daydreaming about the past,
the traffic had begun moving once again, and she was
holding up a long line of vehicles. Swearing under her
breath, she quickly put the car into gear, doing her best
to forget the past—and concentrate on her forthcoming
interview with Fiona Bliss.

However, as it turned out, Leo's fiancée turned out to
be not at all the sort of girl she'd been expecting to meet.

Having finally arrived at the huge, quite hideous
Victorian Gothic house, Alex was startled to be informed
by a starchy, old-fashioned butler that she should *not*
have knocked on the front door but should have taken
herself around to the tradesmen's entrance.

'I believe Miss Fiona is interviewing applicants in the
stable block,' he added with a loud sniff of disapproval,
before firmly shutting the large oak door in her face.

'Charming!' Alex ground out sarcastically, unused to
being treated like a bad smell, or something nasty the
cat had dragged in.

However, determined not to be put off by the first
obstacle, she spent some time exploring the outside of
the enormous, gloomy-looking house and its many out-
buildings. Gazing with a jaundiced eye up at the mass
of ornate turrets and stone battlements, she decided that
it looked far more like her idea of Count Dracula's castle
in Transylvania than an English manor house.

With the pale February afternoon light fading fast, and
just about to admit defeat, Alex finally tracked down
both the large stable block—and Fiona.

'Hello…?' a small voice greeted her as she peered into

the large interior. 'Have you come about my advertise-
ment for a groom?'

As her eyes gradually adjusted to the dim light, Alex
was able to make out the heads of various horses, chew-
ing hay and regarding her with interest over the top of
their individual stable doors. The sound of a sudden clatter of hooves on cobblestones quickly drew her attention
to a chestnut-coloured horse tied up in an open stall, the
animal seeming to tower over the small figure of a girl
busily engaged in stuffing hay into a large net bag.

'Er…no, not exactly,' Alex muttered, wishing she
hadn't bothered to change into a tweed suit and smart,
high-heeled shoes. A pair of old jeans, a thick polo-
necked sweater and her trainers would have been far
more appropriate, she realised, stepping gingerly over
the small puddles of muddy water and bundles of straw
which littered the stone cobbled floor.

Keeping a wary eye on the horse, which seemed to
get larger and more dangerous-looking as she approached the open stall, Alex introduced herself, and explained the reason why she'd made this trip down to
Hampshire.

'I really don't think…I mean…I've never met a journalist before, and…'

'There's no need to panic!' Alex smilingly reassured
the other girl. 'Yes, I'm a reporter on the *Chronicle*. But,
as I also happen to be Leo's stepsister, I'm not likely to
write anything which would upset either his family or
your parents.'

While she'd been speaking, Alex had taken advantage
of the opportunity to take a good, hard look at Leo's
new fiancée. And a frankly depressing sight it turned
out to be.

In the first place, the girl's photographs *definitely* hadn't done her justice. With a heart-shaped face, fresh peaches-and-cream complexion and large, warm brown eyes framed by short, dusky curls, Fiona wasn't just merely pretty...she was outstandingly beautiful!

Towering over the petite girl—whose slim, slight figure and anxious, spaniel-brown eyes were practically guaranteed to bring out the chivalrous, protective feelings in any man—Alex had no problem in understanding exactly *why* Leo was intending to marry Fiona. In fact, she was only surprised that he hadn't placed a wedding ring on her finger long before now.

'If you're really his stepsister, I suppose it must be all right...' Fiona murmured doubtfully, picking up a curry comb and dragging it through the horse's mane. 'But are you *quite* sure that he doesn't mind?' she added breathlessly, biting her lip as she turned to gaze nervously up at Alex. 'I know that he normally loathes having anything to do with the press, and simply *hates* seeing his name in the papers. So...'' Her voice died away, her cheeks flushing a bright crimson as she realised that this tall, elegant blonde girl might think she was being deliberately rude and unhelpful.

'Relax! I'm well aware of Leo's views on the gutter press!' Alex laughed. 'However, I can give you my solemn word of honour that he *has* agreed to let me write about you both, for our Valentine's Day supplement. If it makes you feel any better,' she added, carefully sticking to the truth, 'Leo has insisted that he see and approve of anything I've written before he'll allow it to appear in the newspaper.'

'Oh, well...in that case...' Fiona gave a heavy sigh of relief.

Alex was just wondering why the other girl appeared to be so extraordinarily apprehensive, and almost frightened about Leo's reaction to their meeting, when she found herself shivering in the cold, damp air of the stable.

'I'm absolutely frozen,' she exclaimed. 'Is there anywhere a little bit warmer where we can sit down and have a good talk?'

'There's a nice hot fire in the tack room. We could go there, I suppose…'

'That sounds great. Lead me to it!' Alex said firmly, reluctantly abandoning any hope of being invited to have a comfortable and warming cup of tea, with crumpets and maybe some sinful chocolate cake, in the main house. This girl was clearly so nervous and uncertain about meeting a journalist—let alone spilling the beans about her romance with Leo—that it would be a wonder if they even got as far as the tack room—whatever that might be.

The mystery was soon solved as Fiona led the way into a small room off the stables, whose walls were covered with row upon row of leather bridles and saddles.

Lowering herself onto an old, broken-down leather sofa, Alex warmed her hands at the blaze from the small coal fire, her nose twitching at the various smells of leather, saddle soap and resin as she gazed at the mass of rosettes pinned on a board above the fireplace.

'I heard you were mad on horses. Did you win all those?' she asked, suddenly feeling a lot more cheerful as Fiona produced a Thermos of hot coffee.

The other girl nodded, blushing modestly as she busied herself pouring the steaming liquid into two battered tin mugs.

'I do love horses, of course. But I'm chiefly interested in three-day eventing,' she said, handing a mug to Alex before coming to sit down beside her.

'Eventing...?'

'Well, it basically means that you spend many years patiently training a horse to face three days of hard competition,' Fiona explained. 'On the first day they have to perform a complicated dressage routine. On the second—and much the toughest day—there's an arduous cross-country race over very difficult jumps and obstacles, and finally, on the third day, you have to take your horse into the ring to face a show-jumping exercise against the clock.'

'Training a horse to do all that sounds like hard, tough work,' Alex said slowly. 'And you really love doing that sort of thing?' she added, amazed that anyone so small and light-boned could possibly control a large brute like the horse she'd just seen in the stable.

'Mmm...' Fiona nodded happily. 'It's wonderful! The sense of achievement and sheer thrilling enjoyment you get when you manage to do a clear round over a dangerous and difficult cross-country course is better than...well, better than *anything* else I can think of!'

'Better than sex...?' Alex grinned, considerably interested to note that this girl was obviously far more at home and relaxed in this messy old tack room than she was ever likely to be in the large house.

'Oh—definitely much better!' Fiona agreed with a giggle. 'In fact,' she confided, 'I generally prefer horses to most of the people I know.'

'So...what about Leo? You must prefer him to horses, surely?' Alex queried dryly.

Oh, wow! What wouldn't she give to have the rotten

man here right now? If only to hear about his love-making technique—which had just been so ruthlessly dismissed by his fiancée! That would *definitely* serve the swine right. Especially as Fiona must know what she was talking about. Because it was practically unheard of, nowadays, for two people to become engaged without having been to bed with one another. So...could it be that Leo really *wasn't* such a hot-shot between the sheets after all...?

'Oh, yes, I wasn't referring to Leo. He really is *so* kind,' Fiona breathed, looking positively starry-eyed at the thought of her fiancée.

'How did you meet? Was it at a polo match?' Alex asked, quietly extracting a writing pad from her handbag and being careful not to interrupt the other girl, who was now launched on a long, involved story about her first meeting with Leo.

However, as Fiona continued to rhapsodise about her dear fiancé, Alex had difficulty in reconciling the hard, tough man *she* knew with the version as portrayed by the other girl—where he appeared to be a paragon of all the virtues. Not least of which, it seemed, being his amazing ability to cope with her mother.

Fiona didn't *exactly* say that living cheek by jowl with Ethel Bliss was hell on wheels. Nevertheless, Alex definitely got the message. It seemed that Ethel, nowadays, preferred to live at the family house in London. So, clearly, one of the main reasons behind the girl's urge to bury herself in the country with her beloved horses must be to escape from the clutches of her overbearing, ultra-ambitious mother.

'You won't write anything about Mummy, will you?' Fiona suddenly asked, interrupting her praise of Leo to look at Alex with a scared, frightened expression. 'She'd be very angry, and…'

'Relax—my lips are sealed,' she assured the other girl, not bothering to add that she had no wish to tangle with a woman who sounded like first cousin to a man-eating tiger.

By the time she was driving slowly back to London in the Stygian darkness of the February evening, Alex couldn't help thinking that there was something just a little odd about Leo and Fiona's relationship. She couldn't *quite* put her finger on it, but she definitely had a feeling that…well, that she was somehow missing an important piece of a jigsaw.

Still, it was none of her business. All she had to do was write up the interview. And it wouldn't be hard to portray Fiona in a sympathetic light, since the other girl had been really friendly and they'd got on like a house on fire. In fact, Alex was fast coming to the conclusion that Leo wasn't *nearly* good enough for such a nice girl.

Mentally driving on autopilot as she thought back over the interview, Alex was astounded to find that she'd driven over Chelsea Bridge, and—goodness knows why—had completely failed to turn left at Sloane Square. Since her house was in a cul-de-sac off the King's Road, there seemed no logical reason why her car was now travelling in the opposite direction, towards Knightsbridge.

Oh, well…what the heck? It might be interesting to have a look at Leo's apartment block. Hadn't James Boswell said that he lived in a large penthouse suite? Not that she had any intention of calling in to see the rotten man, of course. Absolutely not! And, in any case, he was probably still in Germany.

However, as she drove past his apartment building, she couldn't help noticing that there definitely seemed to be lights shining brightly on the top storey.

Coming to a halt on the other side of the road, Alex sat drumming her fingers on the wheel for some time. Wrestling with the problem of whether to call in—and get the inevitable blazing row about her visit to Fiona over and done with—or to drive quickly back to her own home and lie low for a while, her eye fell on a buff-coloured folder on the seat beside her. That was the answer, she decided quickly. She would show him the piece she had already done on the two other couples. Not only might it lay his fears to rest, but if he didn't seem in too bad a mood she could then tell him all about her trip down to Hampshire. Right?

Quickly getting out of the car before she lost her nerve, Alex walked swiftly across the road. Having no idea which was Leo's apartment, she rang for the doorman.

'I've just called by to see Mr Leo Hamilton.'

'So...?'

'So, kindly phone up to his apartment,' she retorted, frowning at the burly, uniformed man. 'And say that Miss Alexandra Pemberton would like to see him for a few minutes.'

'I don't really think that Mr Hamilton wishes to...'

'Oh, for goodness' sake—just do it!' she snapped, slipping quickly inside the half-open front door. 'I'm not prepared to stand on the doorstep,' she added as he protested. 'It's absolutely *freezing* out there!'

With a heavy sigh, the doorman walked over to the empty reception desk, picking up the phone and dialling a number. It was some moments before the call was answered, and even from where she stood on the other side of the foyer Alex could hear the sound of Leo's response to her request—which mainly seemed to consist of a loud, exasperated protest at being disturbed.

Maybe it was just as well. It had been a long day, and she really didn't feel like quarrelling with anyone—let alone Leo, she told herself with a tired shrug, turning back towards the large front door.

'He says you're to go on up,' the doorman suddenly announced.

'But I thought...'

The uniformed man grinned. 'You're right. His Nibs doesn't sound in too good a mood. Still, that's your problem, isn't it?' he added, with what she thought of as quite unnecessary cheerfulness, as he opened the lift door and ushered her inside.

As the lift whooshed swiftly up towards the penthouse suite, Alex couldn't help wondering why she obviously had such a tendency to look for trouble. Because, if Leo proved to be as cross and scratchy as he'd sounded down in the foyer, she might well be sorry that she hadn't driven straight back to the quiet comfort of her own home.

CHAPTER FIVE

UGH—OH…! It looked as if deciding to call unexpectedly on Leo had definitely *not* been one of her better
ideas, Alex told herself ruefully.

The sight of his tall figure, stiff with exasperation as
he opened the front door of his penthouse apartment,
waving her impatiently through into the marble-floored
hall was enough to make anyone's spirits sink into their
boots. It only needed another brief, quick glance at those
icy cold green eyes and tight-lipped expression for Alex
to realise that she'd made a bad mistake.

'I only arrived home ten minutes ago. But I should
have known that *you'd* be sure to turn up—just like a
bad penny,' he grated, slamming the door shut behind
her.

'And hello to you, too!' she muttered caustically beneath her breath as he strode past her, leading the way
into a large sitting room. 'By the way—how was
Frankfurt?'

'Frankfurt was no problem. It's the hassle getting to
and from airports that always drives me up the wall,' he
retorted curtly, before spinning around on his heel to
frown down at her. 'How in hell did *you* know that I've
been in Germany?'

Irritated by his less than polite welcome, and feeling
weary herself after the long drive from Hampshire, Alex
was tempted to leave him guessing. However, there was

clearly nothing to be gained by making Leo even more bad tempered than he was already.

'It's very simple,' she shrugged. 'When I saw you at your office, you mentioned that you were flying to Frankfurt on business.'

'So I did.' He grimaced with annoyance. 'I must make a note reminding me to watch out for the pointed, sharp little ears of female journalists.'

Alex gazed steadily back at him, determined not to be riled by his deliberately provocative retort. She'd have to be blind, deaf and dumb not to realise that Leo was obviously spoiling for a fight. So, if she wanted to get anything out of this *very* difficult man, it was beginning to look as though she'd better start pouring a whole lot of oil on these clearly stormy waters.

'Look…why don't you take a deep breath, and cool down?' she suggested calmly. 'I know it's late, and I can see that you're tired. What's more—if it's any comfort—you're not the only one to have had a long, weary day. And the only reason I'm here is because of your insistence on personally seeing and approving of my article for our St Valentine's Day feature.'

'I can give you a good title for the rubbish that you're supposed to be writing. How about, ''The St Valentine's Day Massacre''?' he grated angrily.

'That's not bad—not bad at all,' she murmured, pretending to give his stupid suggestion some serious thought. When he continued to scowl down at her in silence, Alex gave a heavy sigh.

'Oh, come on, Leo—relax! I can't think why you're getting so uptight. Especially as none of your friends are likely to read the *Chronicle*. It's far too much of a downmarket rag for them, right?' she added with a grin. 'Besides, as you can see, I'm not carrying a notebook or recording equipment. Nor—surprise, surprise!—am I wearing a grubby raincoat.' She quickly unbuttoned her suit jacket to display a slim-fitting pale green silk shirt. 'So, what's the problem?'

He gave a reluctant snort of laughter as he viewed the slim curves of the girl standing in front of him.

'*You* are the problem, my dear Alex,' he told her grimly. 'Despite everything you say, I wouldn't trust you any further than I could throw you. Quite frankly, every instinct I possess is telling me, loud and clear, that I've been a fool to even let you in through the door of this apartment.'

'So, you don't want to see what I've written?' she enquired as she held out the buff-coloured file in her hand.

'No, of course I don't!' he snapped irritably, slipping off the jacket of his smart charcoal-grey suit and tossing it onto a nearby chair. 'But it doesn't look as though I've got any choice, does it? However, I'm not doing a damn thing until I've had a long, hot shower and changed my clothes,' he added, quickly undoing the collar of his shirt and removing his tie.

'If you're going to insist on remaining here, you'd better help yourself to a drink,' he continued with a brief, cursory nod towards a drinks tray on a nearby table, before turning on his heel and swiftly leaving the room.

Well—she certainly wouldn't award the rotten man any marks for good manners, Alex told herself grimly as she gazed around the large sitting room.

As much as it might hurt her to say so, she had to admit that Leo clearly had very good taste. The general decor could, of course, have been the work of an ex-

pensive interior designer. However, she suspected that
the large, wide sofas and chairs covered in a cool ivory-
coloured material, and the matching ivory silk curtains
which were simply draped around the enormous floor-
to-ceiling windows, would have been Leo's own choice.

Admiring the rich, glowing colours of the large
Persian rugs scattered over the highly polished wooden
floor, the marble fireplace with its grate full of huge fake
logs, and the oil paintings of eighteenth-century English
and Italian landscapes which decorated the walls, she
wandered over to the drinks tray resting on a slim, mar-
ble-topped table.

Despite fervently wishing that she'd had the sense to
go straight home after her interview with Fiona Bliss,
Alex realised that she now had no choice. She was just
going to have to tough it out and make the best of what
was clearly a bad decision. Maybe a strong slug of alcohol might steady her nerves, she thought, gazing wist-
fully at a large bottle of whisky. But, mindful of the fact
that she was going to have to drive home, she poured
herself a small glass of wine instead.

Drink in hand, she wandered around the large room,
making her way towards one of the large windows. It
was too dark for her to see anything of the large expanse
of Hyde Park, of course. But there must be terrific views
from the terrace, which she could just spot on the other
side of the window and which appeared to run around
the outside of the whole apartment. There was no doubt
that in daylight, and particularly during the summer
months, Leo must be able to enjoy one of the best views
in London.

Deeply envious, she stood staring out at the far distant
twinkling lights of Bayswater and Marble Arch, before

the gleam from a small picture on a nearby wall caught her eye. Moving closer, she realised that it wasn't a painting. Beneath the glass, on a mount of purple velvet, lay a wide, coloured ribbon to which was attached a large, round silver medal.

Of course! She'd completely forgotten that item in James Boswell's gossip column, about Leo winning a silver medal for fencing at the last Olympics. Peering closer, she frowned as she tried to remember what little she knew about the sport.

Other than vague memories of Errol Flynn cutting a dash in old movies, and the fact that nowadays fencers dressed all in white, and wore protective head-covering with black grilles over their faces while brandishing dangerous-looking thin swords, she knew nothing else about the subject. Except, of course, that the days of eighteenth-century duels were long over, and that swords, as such, were no longer used. Didn't they call their weapons something rather esoteric, such as 'foils' and 'rapiers'?

She was still gazing at the silver medal when Leo returned to the room.

Slowly turning around, she viewed his tall, broad-shouldered figure now clothed in a short dark-green towelling robe over long, long tanned legs as he walked barefoot across the floor to pour himself a drink.

'I...er...I didn't know about your Olympic medal. Well, not until yesterday,' she said, trying to tear her eyes away from the disgracefully short dressing gown.

He shrugged. 'There's no reason why you should have heard about it,' he said, dropping cubes of ice into his neat Scotch, and carrying the glass over to where she stood. 'It's very much a minority sport at the best of times. And, in any case, I was lucky.' He turned his head to smile at her. 'The guy I was up against was well ahead on points until he tripped and fell off the platform, spraining an ankle.'

Firmly clutching her glass of wine, Alex struggled to resist the overwhelming, sensual charm exuded by this man—which it seemed he could turn on and off like a lightbulb! Just remember how nasty he was when you first arrived, she shouted silently at herself, gazing helplessly at the dark, curly hairs on his tanned chest clearly visible beneath the open neck of his robe, and the wet black wavy hair falling over his handsome, tanned face. She was forced to admit—if only privately to herself, of course—that he looked absolutely gorgeous, and as sexy as hell!

If this was the sort of outfit that he usually wore when at home in his apartment, it was no wonder that women apparently fell for him in droves. Although, to be fair, his success as a lady-killer was possibly due in equal measure to those sensual, smouldering green eyes beneath their heavy lids.

Taking a deep breath to steady her nerves, she noted that he'd even found time to shave. Well, the swine needn't think that he was going to get *another* chance to kiss her!

She'd always taken care never to get involved with engaged or married men—and she had absolutely *no* intention of starting now, she told herself fiercely. And then was immediately appalled to find herself involuntarily recalling the fiery touch of his lips, and the hard strength of the muscular body, which had been pressed so closely to her own during that mad embrace in his office at the bank.

Was she losing her mind, or what? *Of course* he had no intention of kissing her! In fact, it was clearly the very *last* thing on his mind, she told herself firmly. Both he and she were well aware that the shameful episode yesterday had been merely the product of a sudden spurt of rage on his part, right? Although, she acknowledged glumly, exactly what she'd been doing in responding so ardently to his caresses, she had absolutely *no* idea.

Pull yourself together! she told herself grimly. So he looks fantastic. *So what?* The important thing to remember was that he had a really vile reputation, that he was engaged to Fiona Bliss and, most important of all, she actively disliked the horrid man.

Unfortunately, at that moment the 'horrid man' turned to give her another warm, engaging smile, which practically made her toes curl.

'I'm sorry to have been so bad tempered and grouchy just now. I clearly needed both a shower and this drink!' The ice tinkled in the glass as he raised it to his lips. 'It's been a long, hard day, but I shouldn't have taken it out on you,' he acknowledged, walking over to pick up the buff-coloured file from where she'd left it on a side table.

Stiff with nerves and apprehension, she continued to stand by the window as Leo sat down on a sofa, and quickly read the first, rough draft of her article featuring the romances of the plumber, Dave Morris, and Nigel Adams, her middle-class tax inspector. Almost as if he was deliberately piling on the agony, he then proceeded to read through the manuscript once more, only much slower this time, before closing the file and taking another long sip from his glass.

'There's no need to stand over there like a stag at

bay,' he drawled with a wry grin. 'Why don't you relax, take off your jacket, and come and sit down?'

She shrugged. 'I wasn't sure of your reaction. So I thought that I'd better stay on my feet—all ready to make a quick dash for the door, if necessary,' she admitted, removing her heavy tweed jacket as she slowly crossed the room and lowered herself into a deep, comfortable chair. 'Well, what did you think?'

'Actually, it's not at all bad. In fact, although I'm reluctant to say so, I have to admit that it's surprisingly well written.'

'Gee—thanks!' she muttered caustically.

'There's no need to get on your high horse.' His lips twitched with amusement. 'Since you write for the *Chronicle*, you can hardly blame me for expecting to find myself presented with the usual ghastly, mindless slush normally to be found in newspapers of that type.'

'Hah! That's all you know. Believe me, I wouldn't last five minutes with our new editor, Mike Tanner, if I wrote that sort of drivel,' she retorted. 'And there's no reason for you to sound so surprised, either. My grandmother made sure that I had a decent education. So, why shouldn't I be able to string more than one or two words together?' she demanded indignantly.

He shrugged. 'Of course I was surprised. And why not, when I recall the last time we met? In fact, if I'd been asked to guess how you'd turn out, I'd probably have opted for you joining something like a punk-rock band, or maybe that you'd become a New Age traveller. Neither of which, considering your bizarre appearance at the time, would have been at all surprising,' he added crushingly.

'In any case,' he continued, rising to his feet and

walking swiftly back across the room before she had a chance to say anything in her own defence, 'I'm feeling hungry. So I suggest we leave all further discussion until I've got dressed and fixed us both something to eat.'

'I don't want any of your rotten food!' she shouted after his disappearing figure. But his only reply was a low rumble of laughter, and she found herself left alone in the large room once more.

Maybe it was his reference to her appearance all those years ago, but she seemed unable to prevent the sad, sorry events of that long, hot summer from stealing back into her mind.

Arriving in Tuscany, already bowed down with grief at the loss of her grandmother, she'd been further crushed by her reception at the hands of Eleanor Lucas. It was easy enough now, at a distance of eight years, to understand that the ambassador's wife had, in reality, been the one with the problem. Because anyone who could treat a young teenager with such unkindness and cruelty was undoubtedly in dire need of help.

Unfortunately, despite trying to keep out of everyone's way—as she'd been forcibly instructed to do by Eleanor—almost the first person she'd bumped into had been her stepbrother, Leo Hamilton. And 'bumped' into was the right word, since she'd been bolting down a long, dark corridor, her eyes blinded by tears, when she'd run slap, bang into his tall figure.

'So, you're my newfound stepsister,' he said, putting a comforting arm about her slight, thin, gawky figure as he led her into a nearby sitting room. 'So, what's the problem?'

Quite unable to face telling this wonderfully hand-some man that it was his own mother's cruel, sarcastic tongue from which she was fleeing, Alex mumbled something about being unhappy with her appearance.

'Well…dying your hair that awful colour obviously wasn't too clever,' he agreed calmly. 'But it's hardly the end of the world.'

Continuing to talk calmly and kindly to her, he pointed out that probably her best option was to cut it all off as soon as possible. 'What colour is your hair normally?' he asked, and, when she told him that it was 'sort of fair', he cupped his hands about her head, staring intently down into her face.

'I'll tell you what, Alexandra,' he said slowly. 'I'm willing to bet that in a few years' time you'll turn out to be a raving beauty. With those lovely blue eyes and a mass of blonde hair—you'll be a complete knockout!'

'Really…?' she breathed, enchanted by this new vision of herself as a sort of *femme fatale*.

'Really and truly!' he laughed, bending forward to plant a brief kiss on her nose, before going off to join his friends in the swimming pool.

And that small, casual act of kindness—which he'd undoubtedly forgotten all about by the time he reached the pool—was enough to immediately plunge Alex into the heady delights and deep misery of falling in love for the very first time.

With his extraordinarily handsome face, and lock of dark hair falling over his brow, he was obviously the very embodiment of the thrillingly wicked Lord Byron, whose poetry she was studying at school. Although Leo, as far as she was concerned, was very far from being 'mad, bad, and dangerous to know'. *He* was obviously a true hero—the perfect, gentle knight of all her romantic fantasies, whom she could only hope to worship from afar. Until…as in all the very best fairy-tales…she somehow managed to save his life. Whereupon he would undoubtedly give her a chaste kiss and claim her for his bride.

The only trouble with this scenario was that, when Eleanor did eventually drag her off to the local hair-dresser, and her hair was cut as short as possible, Alex was convinced that she now looked even worse than ever.

She spent long hours in front of her mirror, tugging at hair which was barely an inch long and bore a strong resemblance to an American crew-cut. It was practically impossible to imagine Leo wanting to know her—let alone claim her for his bride. Which was why she'd done her very best to keep out of his way. But, strangely, as that hot summer holiday continued, it seemed that de-spite her best efforts to avoid him she was continually coming across his tall, handsome figure. And, since he lived in the house, he was often witness to her increasing quarrels with his mother.

Alex had, by then, got used to the fact that there was nothing she could do to please Eleanor Lucas. Sir Geoffrey would often shield the young girl from the worst onslaughts, but he was often away, and there was no one else with the authority to check the older wom-an's unkind tongue. Although, to give him his due, Leo did frequently step in and take the part of his stepsister. But as he, too, was often away staying with friends, or out at late-night parties, Alex was left to stand her own corner, doing her feeble best not to be ground down by Eleanor.

The episode of the missing brooch, whereby Alex sud-denly found herself being arrested as a common thief and taken to the local police station, was still enough to give her nightmares all these years later. It hadn't, of course, been the fault of the local police. There had been little they could do—not once Lady Lucas, the wife of a distinguished ambassador, had laid charges against a girl living in her house.

In a state of total panic and terror, Alex was half out of her mind by the time Leo turned up. He quickly secured her release by producing the missing brooch, which had eventually been found by one of the servants where the careless older woman had left it—in her bathroom!

He carried her back into the house and up to her room, but she was terrified of being left alone in the house with his mother. After making sure that she had some food on a tray, and faithfully promising that she would be quite safe, he had to leave to attend a party on the other side of the valley.

During the long evening in which, thankfully, the dreaded Eleanor had not made an appearance, Alex lay shivering on her bed, weeping with misery and desolation. And it was in a state of tearful exhaustion that Leo found her on his return to the villa much later that night.

Maybe he felt real concern, and had only meant to offer genuine comfort to the distressed young girl. But, whatever his intentions, as soon as his arms closed gently about her trembling figure the atmosphere in the moonlit bedroom suddenly became charged with a crackling electric tension. Even Alex, who had no conception of the forces which became unleashed by the close proximity of their two bodies, realised that something strange was happening to both Leo and herself.

With only the shafts of moonlight to illuminate her

shadowy figure on the bed, and the surrounding darkness shielding her cropped hair from his view, Alex was free to imagine that she really was the beautiful princess of her teenage dreams, being awoken by a tender kiss from her handsome prince. In a dream-like state, suspended midway between reality and fantasy, she found herself ardently responding to his warm embrace, her lips opening beneath his, actively welcoming the pressure of the strong, firm body whose arms were tightening convulsively about her slim figure. But it was her own soft moans of delight breaking into the heavy silence which brought an immediate and shocking end to the enchantment.

'Oh—*my God*!'

Even after all these years, Alex could still hear and see in her mind's eye the cry of horror as Leo leaped swiftly off the bed, and the savage expression of disgust on his face, clearly illuminated by the moonlight, as he told her never, *ever* to come near him again!

'P-please...please don't say that, Leo,' she begged tearfully. 'I love you. I truly love you—with all my heart!'

'Don't be stupid! You've no idea what you're talking about,' he retorted curtly. 'Believe me, that wasn't "love".' He gave a cruel, sardonic laugh. 'When you're older, you'll realise it meant nothing. Absolutely nothing more than a case of brief sexual attraction. So, kindly remember that technically I'm almost your stepbrother— and don't play games until you're old enough to understand the rules,' he added with terrifying menace, before turning to stride rapidly from the room.

Quite how she got through the rest of the night, Alex had no idea. When she awoke, a maid informed her that

Leo had left the villa earlier that morning. And, following her forced departure back to England a few days later, she had never seen him again. Not, that is, until she'd marched into his office all these years later.

Immersed in her unhappy memories of the past, Alex was startled out of her reverie by the sudden reappearance of the man she'd fallen so desperately in love with eight years ago.

'There was only the usual awful food on the aeroplane. Which means that I'm now absolutely starving,' Leo announced. 'So, I'm going to knock something up in the kitchen. Do you feel like joining me?'

The memories of Tuscany were still so strongly fixed in her mind that Alex had difficulty pulling herself together. 'Er…no, I don't think… I mean, it's really time I went home,' she muttered, struggling to rise from the low, comfortable chair.

Unfortunately, as she gazed around the room, wondering where she'd left her handbag, she was suddenly betrayed as her stomach gave a loud rumble of acute hunger.

Leo laughed. 'You may not want any food—but your insides clearly have other ideas!' He grinned. 'When did you last eat?'

Trying to pummel her brain into some kind of working order, Alex could only remember having a late-morning sandwich before driving off to see Fiona Bliss. So, it looked as though all she'd had since then was a hot cup of coffee, and a glass of wine here in Leo's apartment.

'If it's taking you that long to answer my question then you're clearly in need of a meal,' Leo announced, taking no notice of her protests as he firmly carted her off to the large kitchen.

'That was really great!' Alex sighed some considerable time later as she viewed the empty plate in front of her. 'I hate to say it, but you're obviously a really good cook.'

'Gee—thanks!' he drawled, grinning as he accurately mimicked her own words from earlier, when he'd expressed surprise at her ability to string more than one or two words together.

'Well, you might have known that I *could* write, since that's obviously the way I earn my living,' she pointed out mildly. 'But, since I'm not clairvoyant, how could I have possibly guessed that a stuffy City banker—who also, according to Fleet Street gossip, has a really *terrific* reputation as a Casanova—would turn out to be a really great chef?'

'Gee—thanks. *Again!*' he ground out, clearly not so amused this time. 'As for my so-called reputation…I can assure you that it's highly exaggerated. Quite a work of fiction, in fact.'

'Yes, well…' She took another sip of the really excellent wine. 'Never mind, Leo. Once the word gets around that you cook like a dream, I don't suppose you'll have *any* problem with your love life.'

'I can assure you that there's *no* problem with my love life!' he snapped irritably.

'But I thought you just said—?'

'Rubbish! I was merely pointing out…' He paused, catching the gleam of laughter in her eyes. 'Ouch! I walked straight into that one, didn't I?' He shook his head with annoyance and self-disgust. 'It's clear that not only should I watch my tongue—but that you, my dear Alex, have had quite enough to drink,' he drawled in an icy tone of voice. 'So I think it's time we had some coffee in the other room, don't you?'

Oh, Lord! The awful man was quite right. Unfortunately, the smoked salmon tagliatelle, followed by grilled king prawns and a delicious salad—which Leo had seemed to conjure up out of thin air—had been so scrumptious that she'd hardly noticed how much wine she'd been drinking. Which meant that she was now in no fit state to drive home. What on earth was she going to do?

It was a question that was still buzzing intermittently in her head as she sipped her cup of strong black coffee in the sitting room some minutes later. Maybe, if she concentrated on putting as much caffeine into herself as possible, she'd be able to sober up by the time it came to drive home?

Unfortunately, while the coffee was certainly helping her to feel a lot more wide awake, the alcohol still coursing through her veins seemed to have the disastrous effect of loosening her tongue. Which meant that, almost before she knew what she was doing, she found herself telling him all about her plan for the three couples to attend a St Valentine's Day ball.

'That's all I need,' Leo muttered grimly.

Under normal circumstances, he would have been prepared to quite cheerfully wring this damned girl's neck! However, since he had absolutely no intention of attending any stupid ball—and there was little or no chance of Alex, at this late stage, being able to get hold of any tickets—there seemed little point in getting too annoyed about the situation. Particularly since he had every intention of having a long talk on the phone to Fiona first thing tomorrow morning. Once Ms Pemberton found herself unable to either interview Fiona or to gain any real co-operation from himself, this whole stupid idea would, hopefully, soon be dead and buried.

The fact that he found Alex quite extraordinarily attractive was neither here nor there. Because there was *no way* he was prepared to allow himself to be used as a stooge merely to save her career.

And there was clearly no reason for him to feel concerned or even guilty if she *did* lose her job, he told himself firmly. She'd been quite ruthless, particularly in her attempt to blackmail him into agreeing to co-operate with that crazy article of hers. On top of which, Alexandra Rothstein—or Alex Pemberton, as she now liked to call herself—was an extremely rich young girl. So, even if the *Chronicle* dispensed with her services, it was hardly the end of the world. It wasn't as if she was likely to find herself starving in a garret, for heaven's sake.

While Alex was well aware that she'd drunk too much wine, she was still sober enough to note that Leo didn't seem to be particularly worried about attending the ball. Maybe it would be a good idea to get rid of all the bad news at once?

'Well, I appreciate you taking it on the chin like this,' she told him with a relieved smile. 'I was certain that you'd go up in a puff of smoke on hearing about the ball. Which is why I made sure of choosing the dance which your mother's organising, for the National Society for Orphaned Children.'

'*What...?*'

'I don't know why you're looking so upset,' she

grumbled. 'Especially since I spent a lot of time trying to get hold of enough tickets. Most balls are sold out at this time of the year, you know.'

'Yes, I was aware of that fact,' he ground out through clenched teeth.

'Well…you might look a bit more grateful, Leo, because I took a lot of trouble to choose a ball where you *wouldn't* stand out like a sore thumb. I mean, your friends aren't likely to be too surprised if they hear that you turned up to support your mother, are they?'

Unfortunately, the damned girl was quite right! In fact, if he wasn't so angry about being out-manoeuvred, he might even be prepared to admit that if he *had* to go to a Valentine's ball she'd managed to choose the only one he'd be prepared to attend. Which didn't make such a bitter pill any easier to swallow.

'You certainly seem to have been very busy on my behalf,' Leo drawled in a dangerously soft, bland voice. 'While we're at it, are there any other arrangements you'd like to tell me about? Any small detail that might require my help, hmm…?'

'No, I don't think so,' Alex told him, suddenly feeling a lot more cheerful and confident.

Obviously Leo couldn't be expected to be too thrilled about having to attend his mother's shindig. But, all in all, he seemed to be taking everything very calmly. Of course, she hadn't yet told him about seeing Fiona earlier today. But he was obviously in such a good mood that it looked as if this was a perfect opportunity to break the bad news. Though she hadn't yet worked out one or two minor arrangements…

'Oh, yes—there is just one thing,' she added quickly. 'I haven't yet sorted out the exact time we're all going to be turning up at the dance. As you probably know, it's on a Thursday, so the traffic shouldn't be too bad. I'll have to let you and Fiona know about the arrangements later this week. OK?'

'Ah…well, I think you may find that you've a slight problem there,' he told her with grim satisfaction. 'I'm not at all sure that dear Fiona will be able to make the ball, after all. It's very sad, of course.' He shook his head sorrowfully. 'I know that she'd like to be able to co-operate with your plans, but…'

'There's no need to worry about your fiancée,' Alex assured him earnestly. 'Fiona has already told me that she's quite happy to go along with all the arrangements. Just as long as we keep awful old Ethel well out of the picture, of course!'

'What?'

'There's no need to shout!' Alex protested, suddenly realising that she might have been just a *little* too optimistic about Leo's good humour—and his likely reaction to the news that she'd seen Fiona Bliss.

'Are you seriously trying to tell me…?'

'Calm down! There's no need to get excited,' she said quickly, wincing at the expression of outrage and fury on his handsome face. 'Yes, I went down to Hampshire to see Fiona today—and you'll be glad to hear that we got on really well.'

'Why should I be "glad to hear" anything from you?' he demanded furiously. 'You…you stupid, interfering girl! Why in hell can't you mind your own damn business?'

'Now—*just* a minute!' she hissed angrily. 'I've never known anyone so certain that *they* are always right, or anyone so stiff with self-righteous pride. You're clearly the sort of guy who'd give hubris a far worse name than it has already! Well, maybe it's time you realised that you aren't *quite* as smart and clever as you'd like to think you are, Leo. Because I was perfectly well aware that you regarded me as stupid, and that you'd have no problem in keeping Fiona under wraps and well out of sight. Which is *precisely* why I went down to see her today. *And* let me tell you,' Alex ground out through gritted teeth, 'I reckon that she's an idiot to be throwing herself away on a…a raving Casanova like you. In fact, why she seems to think that you're the cat's pyjamas, I have absolutely *no* idea!'

'How *dare* you talk to me like that!' he roared angrily. 'And will you kindly *stop* calling me a "Casanova"?'

'According to James Boswell—and *he* ought to know—you've had more girls lining up to climb into bed with you than he's had hot dinners!'

'Oh—*really*…?' he ground out savagely. 'Well, in that case…what have I got to lose…?'

Later, try as she might, Alex was never able to work out the *exact* sequence of what happened next. It must have had something to do with Leo's fast, lightning-quick reactions as a fencer, but quite how he managed the feat, she had no idea.

One moment she was sitting bolt upright on a sofa, giving the awful man a piece of her mind. And then…almost faster than the speed of light…she found herself being dragged swiftly through the air—coming down to land on a sofa on the other side of the room. And, before she could even catch her breath, she found herself firmly pinned to the cushions by Leo's long, hard body.

'I've had it! I'm simply not prepared to put up with

any more of your nonsense,' he growled menacingly as she gazed helplessly up at him, her brain still in a complete whirl. 'You've been nothing but a prickly thorn in my flesh for the past eight years. And it's about time I plucked you out.'

'What...what in hell are you talking about?' she yelled, finding her voice at last.

'I'm talking about you and me, Alex,' he breathed, so quietly that she still wasn't sure that she heard him correctly as his mouth came firmly down on her trembling lips.

CHAPTER SIX

'YOU'D better hurry, Alex. Mike Tanner was demanding to know where you were over five minutes ago. Incidentally, the word is that our dear editor is on the warpath.'

'Oh, great! That's all I need,' Alex muttered, searching frantically through the pile of papers on her desk. 'Do you know why he wants to see me?'

'No, sorry—I haven't a clue.' Her friend Lizzy shrugged, sitting down at the desk beside Alex and frowning at the computer screen in front of her. 'I feel totally uninspired today,' she moaned. 'What do you think of the headline; "Vicar says Vice is Nice"…?'

'Not a lot.' Alex gave her a brief, fleeting grin, before hurrying across the enormously large, noisy room towards a glass-walled suite of offices.

It now seemed that Mike Tanner was busy, in conference with one of the newspaper's lawyers. However, catching sight of Alex through the glass partition, he quickly held up his two hands, the outstretched fingers indicating that he would see her in ten minutes.

Walking slowly back across the room crowded with desks and the noisy output of many journalists, most of them shouting at one another, she finally reached the sanctuary of her own corner.

Almost groaning aloud at her own folly, she searched frantically in her handbag for the small bottle of aspirins which she'd borrowed from her colleague, Tessa, only two days ago. It seemed almost impossible to believe that so much had happened in such a short space of time. And she'd never had so many bad, thumping headaches in her life!

But that's your own problem—right? she told herself grimly, quickly grabbing the mug of cold coffee on her desk and swiftly swallowing the pills. There wasn't a chance that the aspirins would start acting before she'd have to go and see Mike Tanner, of course. Still, they might eventually help to lessen the effects of what was, alas, a full-blown hangover.

How *could* she have been so foolish? Quite certain that she hadn't drunk *all* that much, Alex could only assume that her recent bout of flu had left her dangerously susceptible to the dire effects of alcohol. But it didn't really matter what had led to her disgraceful conduct last night. In fact, she was so ashamed of her own behaviour that she'd hardly been able to look at herself in the mirror this morning.

During that cataclysmic row with Leo, when she'd clearly been in the grip of some totally rash, alcohol-induced euphoria, she'd obviously been in no fit state to realise that the scene could only end in tears.

'In vino veritas'—in wine is truth—might be an old Latin tag, but it was obviously as true today as it had been about two thousand years ago. Because there was no escaping the fact that her tongue had been loosened by the amount of alcohol she'd consumed, prompting her not only to tell all about her arrangements for the St Valentine's Day Ball, but also to give Leo her full, frank views on both his reputation and Fiona Bliss's folly in wishing to become engaged to him.

And the net result of such stupidity…? Alex groaned,

burying her face in her hands for a moment, hardly able to contemplate her temporary bout of reckless insanity.

No wonder Leo had gone bananas! When she'd found herself lying on the sofa, pinned beneath his long, hard and very angry figure, she'd clearly had no one but herself to blame. As his dark head had come down towards her, Alex had realised that there was no escape. And, although fear and panic at the forces she'd almost deliberately provoked had been rapidly clearing the fumes of alcohol from her brain, it had proved to be far, *far* too late.

Struggle as she might, Alex had realised she was helpless, totally at his mercy, as his mouth had crushed hers in a kiss of devastating intensity, forcing her lips apart to allow his tongue to conduct a ravaging exploration— a punishing, deliberate invasion of overwhelming sexuality.

Time had had no meaning, hours had seemed to pass by before the relentlessly hard pressure eased, and he'd at last slowly raised his head to stare at the girl lying beneath him.

Shattered and totally speechless, Alex had quickly clamped her eyelids shut on the weak tears she'd been able to feel threatening to flow down her cheeks any minute. But not before the sight of his tense, rigid expression had been indelibly printed on her brain, the green eyes appearing to be almost as confused and bewildered as her own. Despite her own shock and misery, she'd been able to hear him swearing violently under his breath, and had felt the surprisingly gentle touch of his hand as he brushed a stray, damp lock of hair from her brow.

She'd managed to give a weak groan of protest as he'd

lowered his dark head once more, and it had been some time before her dazed mind had realised that he was merely softly kissing away the droplets of tears on her damp, spiky eyelashes, pressing gentle kisses on the outline of her trembling lips. The soothing, warm touch of his lips on hers had seemed to possess a serene, tranquil sensuality that had quivered through her body—an ever-increasingly heady force that she'd seemed powerless to resist.

Almost without knowing what she'd been doing, her lips had parted beneath the gentle yet insistent seduction of his probing tongue, the deepening kiss seeming to project her senses and emotions into the stratosphere. Somehow, it had seemed as if a swift tide of erotic pleasure was sweeping through her veins, responding instinctively to the arousal of the hard, muscular body holding her ruthlessly captive on the soft cushions. And then she'd become aware that he was withdrawing from her, had heard a slight groan and a heavy sigh as his lips had left hers, and had felt the release of his body's heavy pressure as he'd risen slowly to his feet and walked away across the room.

Forcing herself to open her eyes, she'd seen that Leo was now standing by the fireplace, one foot raised on the ornate copper fender as he'd stared steadfastly down into the flames.

Full realisation of what had just taken place had suddenly hit her, like a hard blow to the solar plexus. Breathless, her cheeks burning with embarrassment and mortification, it had been all she could do not to groan out loud. Oh, Lord! The whole disastrous episode had been one hundred per cent her own fault. First of all drinking too much, and then stupidly provoking Leo to retaliate... She'd quickly turned her head away, clamping her eyes shut and drawing her knees up into a foetal position as she'd desperately tried to think what to do.

Unfortunately, there had been *nothing* that she could either say or do which wouldn't have made the whole situation twenty times worse than it had been already. Eventually realising that she couldn't stay huddled on the sofa much longer, Alex had taken a deep breath and had rolled over, struggling to her feet.

A thick, heavy silence had seemed to fill the huge room.

'I...I'm sorry...' she managed to whisper at last, her cheeks flaming with crimson once more as she realised that not only was her tweed skirt practically hitched up around her waist, but that she had no excuse nor, indeed, rational explanation for the extraordinary explosion of fierce, raw desire which had gripped her only a few moments ago.

As Leo continued to stand staring blindly down at the flames, it suddenly seemed desperately important that he should understand that she didn't normally behave like this. Indeed, having always prided herself on a cool, sophisticated approach towards her various boyfriends in the past, Alex was now totally at a loss to account for the utterly inexplicable surge of almost overpowering passion which had been triggered by the intimate closeness of his strong, muscular body.

'I'm sorry...' she muttered again, quickly pulling down her skirt. 'I really don't...I mean, I'm not in the habit of doing this sort of thing,' she added lamely, her hands all fingers and thumbs as she struggled to tuck her thin silk shirt inside the waistband of her skirt.

'There is no need for you to apologise,' Leo said at

last, his voice and face devoid of all expression as he turned to walk across the room and pour them both a drink.

'Oh, no, I couldn't really… I've already had far too much…' she protested as he held out a glass towards her.

'Don't be stupid, Alex,' he rasped. 'It's far too late to worry about a small trifle like that. In any case, I've already decided to send you home by taxi,' he added with a heavy sigh. 'So, let's not have any more arguments, hmm? Besides, you look as if you could do with a stiff drink.'

Oh, Lord—he was right! She must look a fright. After quickly asking for directions, she seized her handbag and practically flew out of the room. A few moments later, she was locking the door of the palatial bathroom firmly behind her.

A swift glance in the mirror was enough to confirm her worst fears. She looked a total and utter mess! Opening her handbag, she was relieved to see that it held her brush and comb, as well as her make-up bag. And this was definitely a time to wear as much warpaint as possible, she told herself glumly. Although, how she was going to get herself out of this extremely awkward situation—and at the same time manage to retain any dignity—she had absolutely no idea.

Quickly drawing a brush through her heavy, sunstreaked fair hair, she gazed around at the pale cream marble walls, the gold taps, and fluffy thick cream towels which were reflected in the cleverly lit mirrored walls of the bathroom.

Having brought her thick mane of hair under some control, Alex was just about to renew her make-up when her eyes were drawn to some heavy-looking crystal bottles on the shelf beside her. Maybe it was her insatiable curiosity which had first led her into the field of journalism, but she couldn't resist picking up one of the crystal jars. Removing the stopper and inhaling the rich aroma of musk, sandalwood and other spices, she instantly recognised the scent of Leo's cologne.

Quite suddenly, the conflicting emotions which she had experienced in his embrace, only a few minutes ago, swiftly rose up to torment her. There seemed little she could do to banish the throbbing, almost sick excitement now zig-zagging through her body as she recalled the way she'd been crushed so tightly against his hard chest...the erotic touch of his lips, and...

With a low groan, Alex quickly turned on the tap, splashing her flushed cheeks with cold water and roughly towelling them dry as she tried to wipe the erotic, sensual visions from her distraught mind.

Despite renewing her make-up, and trying to make herself look as calm and sophisticated as possible, it was only with a super-human effort of will that she forced herself to leave the sanctuary of the bathroom and make her way back into Leo's sitting room. As he handed her a drink, and blandly informed her that he had already phoned for a taxi to take her home, she could only be grateful that he appeared to have no wish to rub salt in her festering wounds.

'Since we both, for one reason or another, seem to have lost control of our normal, sensible selves, there seems no point in discussing what happened just now,' he drawled tonelessly. 'After all, as I think I said in my office the other day, who can explain the inexplicable?'

It's all right for him, she thought gloomily. He probably has encounters like this with various women every day of the week! In fact, other than some stern lines about his mouth and a muscle beating in his rigid jaw, Leo seemed to be behaving as if what had just taken place was an everyday occurrence as far as he was concerned. Well, that's bloody men all over! she told herself morosely.

Burying her nose in her glass, Alex was highly relieved when the doorman rang through to the apartment to say that a taxi was waiting for her downstairs. And, despite the fact that Leo insisted on escorting her down to the foyer, she could only imagine that he, like herself, must have breathed a thankful sigh of relief as the vehicle in which she was travelling sped off down the street.

It wasn't until she was almost home that Alex realised she would have to face all the hassle of having to remove her car from where she'd left it outside Leo's apartment some time tomorrow.

And she had, therefore, been amazed and deeply thankful to find it parked outside her front door early this morning. Quite *how* Leo had managed to organise this, she had no idea—and she certainly wasn't going to ask. Because the least contact she had with him in the future, the better.

'Hurry up, Alex! What on earth's got into you today?' Lizzy's voice broke urgently through her deep, gloomy introspection.

'Hmm...?'

'For heaven's sake—get a move on!' her friend hissed urgently. 'Can't you hear Mike Tanner shouting the place down? He wants you in his office, and I *really* wouldn't keep him waiting, if I were you.'

'Oh, Lord!' Alex breathed, seizing up the buff folder and her notepad and pencil before rushing towards Mike's office.

Luckily, Mike Tanner didn't seem to be too upset at her late arrival. In fact, it seemed as though the editor was in unusually high spirits.

'Well, now, Alex. How's your St Valentine's Day article coming along?' he enquired jovially.

'Actually, I'm doing rather well,' she told him, trying to sound bright-eyed and bushy-tailed. Because, certainly as far as the *Chronicle* was concerned, the fact that she now fervently wished she'd never had the bright idea in the first idea was of absolutely no interest whatsoever. 'I've got all three couples sorted out now, and have already written two thirds of the article,' she said, placing the buff folder on his desk. 'I just have to type up my notes on Leo Hamilton and Fiona Bliss—and then it's all over bar the shouting.'

'Excellent…really excellent news,' Mike murmured, practically rubbing his hands with glee. 'And you've arranged for everyone to attend an up-market Valentine's Day ball?'

She nodded. 'Yes. I thought it might be a nice touch to get tickets for the bash organised by Leo Hamilton's mother, for an orphaned children's charity.'

Mike beamed at her. 'Well done. In fact, it sounds as though you've got everything so well under control that there'll be no trouble in bringing everything forward by one week.'

'What…?' She stared at him in consternation.

'Yes. I want your article on my desk tomorrow afternoon. We're going to run the romance supplement *before* Valentine's Day!'

'But, why…? Surely it doesn't make sense…' she protested.

Mike gave a snort of sardonic laughter. 'Oh, yes it does! Especially when I tell you that an old friend of the owner of the newspaper has been trying to bring a lot of pressure to bear in an effort to put a stop to the whole feature. Well, as I've just told the lawyer, I'm not having any of *that* nonsense!' he said forcibly, jabbing a fat, half-smoked cigar firmly between his teeth, before rising to his feet and pacing about the room.

She frowned. 'But I don't understand why…'

'Oh, come on, Alex! There's only one person with enough reason—and also enough social and financial clout—to want to stop the article!' He paused for a moment. But when she continued to gaze at him blankly, he gave another snort of laughter. 'It has to be that stepbrother of yours, Leo Hamilton. Doesn't it?'

When she continued to stare at him in silence, desperately trying to grasp the facts of the situation, Mike continued impatiently. 'There's no need to look so upset. As I told the proprietor on the phone just a few minutes ago, I didn't agree to take on the editorship of this newspaper in order to make sure that his friends and acquaintances had a good press. As I pointed out, he can't have it both ways. If he wants a successful paper with a rising circulation—he can get off my back!'

'And has he…has he agreed to get off your back?' she asked in a small voice.

Mike laughed. 'Of course he has. The guy isn't a complete idiot, and he knows how much I relish a good fight.' He chomped happily on his cigar. 'Oh, yeah. Our revered proprietor caved in without a fight. And I should hope so too. I'm damn well not putting up with any censorship of *my* paper, thank you very much!'

However, as Mike then pointed out, he wasn't going to take any chances, since past experience had shown him that the Leo Hamiltons of this life didn't give up so easily. Which was why, he told her, he'd decided to bring one of the articles forward by one week.

'We'll print all the nonsense about these couples' romances in this Saturday's supplement—and your report on the Valentine's Ball, together with a large photo spread, the following week.'

'The timescale is a bit tight,' she warned.

'So what?' he demanded.

She shrugged. 'OK…OK, no problem,' she muttered, anxious to prove that she was up to the job. And then, since he seemed to be in such a good humour at having vanquished the owner of the newspaper, she decided to chance her arm. 'We're going to need a photographer, of course. Can I have Sid the Snapper?' she asked, mentioning the nickname of Sid Reilly, the paper's top photo journalist.

'Yeah—if he's free. Why not? Just make sure of bringing home the bacon,' was Mike's parting shot as she quickly hurried out of his office.

Never mind 'bringing home the bacon'. She now faced an almost insuperable task. She *had* to get an interview with Leo, because she just didn't have enough background material—or anything about his hopes, aspirations, et cetera. Unfortunately, if it really *was* Leo who'd put pressure on the newspaper's proprietor—and she couldn't think of anyone else who'd be interested in doing so—then the idea of gaining any co-operation

from him was a total waste of time. But she clearly had
no alternative except to at least try to contact him.

Even after drinking a mug of hot coffee and trying to
psych herself up for the phone call, Alex still felt positively sick as she forced herself to dial Leo's number at
the bank. And, as she ought to have realised, the first
hurdle she had to get over was his personal assistant,
Dora.

There was no mistaking the frozen, icy tones as Leo's
faithful, super-loyal assistant informed Alex that he was
not available.

'Oh, come on, Dora—give me a break,' she pleaded.
But all to no avail. Even when she offered fulsome apologies for having pretended to be Fiona Bliss on her visit
to Leo's office, his clearly devoted assistant wouldn't
budge.

'Damn!' she muttered, leaning back in her chair and
wondering how on earth she could solve this impasse. It
was no good trying to see him at his office. After her
last attempt, she was quite certain that she'd be thrown
out on her ear before she even got as far as the lift. She
knew from James Boswell that his home telephone number was ex-directory...so what the heck was she going
to do?

It was the thought of James Boswell, and his likely
contacts, which put a fresh idea into her head. A few
minutes later, Alex was perched on the edge of his desk,
explaining her problem and asking for his help.

'No way!' James lifted his hands in horror. 'What
you're asking me to do is one hundred per cent illegal.
Besides, why *should* I put myself out for you?'

It was obvious from his sulky, disgruntled attitude that
the gossip columnist still harboured a grudge about her

hitherto unknown relationship with Leo Hamilton. And he certainly wasn't going to help her—not without some very strong inducement.

He was quite right, of course. Because what she was suggesting was highly illegal. However, she knew that, if he wanted to, he could get hold of Leo's private telephone number at the bank. And Leo *must* have one, if only for all those intimate calls to his many girlfriends which he certainly wouldn't want going through the bank's switchboard, she told herself sourly. She definitely remembered seeing two phones on his desk, so it was just a case of somehow, by hook or by crook, getting hold of that important number.

Studying James from beneath her eyelashes for a moment, and noting the stubborn cast of the man's jaw, she realised that he wouldn't change his mind. Not unless she could offer him a strong incentive to do so.

'OK, James.' She gave him her best version of a wide, beaming smile. 'I *really* want that number. So, I guess it's trade-off time, isn't it?'

He shrugged. But she could see from the way his long nose twitched, and the slight gleam in his eye, that he might be prepared to do a deal.

'How about if I give you the inside track on Robert Fraser's new girlfriend, who's a well-known film star? And, exactly *how* Sir Paul Norton cheated his old aunt out of all her money in pursuit of his first million. And I *mean* cheated,' she added grimly. 'The poor old girl was left destitute. Her friends and a few relatives have rallied round now, of course, but I honestly don't have the slightest compunction in throwing *him* to the wolves!'

Although James pretended not to be interested, Alex could see that she definitely had him on the hook.

'Well…we could have a deal going here,' he admitted. 'I'll also want the background to your friend Sophie's romance with that high-flying Eurobond dealer, Joe Parker—and exactly why she's recently dropped him like a hot potato.'

'Absolutely not!' Alex snapped. 'I don't mind ratting on those two guys I mentioned earlier, because they're nasty bits of work and deserve everything that they get. But if I catch you trying to dig into Sophie's private life, I'll—'

'Relax!' he interjected quickly. 'I've got the message, OK?' he added with a slight laugh, before giving a shrug of his shoulders and saying that he would see what he could do to get hold of Leo's private number.

'You've got ten minutes. After that, our deal's off,' she told him firmly, getting up and walking back to her desk.

Considerably ashamed of the fact that she seemed to be turning into a regular blackmailer, Alex sat down at her desk, staring blindly at the computer screen in front of her. Even if her gamble paid off, and James Boswell came through with the elusive phone number, there was no guarantee that Leo would talk to her. And, of course, the very *last* thing she wanted was to have any more contact with him.

Leo had pointed out that there was no explaining the inexplicable, and he certainly seemed to be right. Because, while she'd had her moments in the past, of course, she'd never found anyone who'd 'made the earth move', as portrayed in all the very best romantic novels. Even the kisses of her last boyfriend, who'd been a very nice man indeed, hadn't produced more than a slight increase in her pulse rate, his lovemaking meaning no more to her than a mild, pleasurable experience.

So how could she possibly explain the earth-shattering, positively bone-melting passion and excitement which seemed to instantly well up inside her at the touch of Leo's lips and body?

He's just a practised seducer—that's all there is to it! she told herself desperately. He obviously has this effect on *every* woman he comes across—and if you don't watch out you'll just be another notch on his bedpost!

The solution to her problem was quite clear. She'd obviously been temporarily out of her mind over the last few days. Therefore, the only sensible answer was to regard the whole affair as just one of those things best forgotten. Especially as there was no need for her to have any further close contact. She'd make her phone call to Leo, she would attend the dance with the three couples—and that would be that.

Alex sighed. It sometimes seemed to her that she spent most of her life staring at the screen of a computer, either here at home or in the newspaper office. Leaning back in her chair, she gazed around at the book-lined shelves of her study. If only she had the aid of some of those well-known authors, she might have a chance of producing something readable. But, despite having written at least three completely different drafts about the romance between Fiona Bliss and Leo, each one seemed to be more turgid and positively dripping with syrup than the last.

'It's all that rotten man's fault!' she grumbled out loud. There had been absolutely no need for him to have been so foul on the phone this afternoon. After all, she had a job to do—and they both knew it.

Well…maybe she was being unfair, Alex told herself with a sigh, getting up from behind her desk and walking over to the window. After all, she certainly wouldn't want anything written about her own private life, she acknowledged with another heavy sigh as she stared down into the garden next door, the bright moonlight sparkling on the trees and shrubs covered with a heavy frost.

Once James Boswell had come through with the required telephone number—as she'd known that he would—it had taken an enormous effort of will for her to find the courage to lift the receiver and dial through to Leo's private office. And even more courage, she reminded herself grimly, not to slam the phone down on his furious response to her call. To say that he had *not* been a happy man was to put it mildly!

'This is all your fault,' he'd ground out furiously, after reluctantly listening to her explanation of why her editor was bringing forward the article and publishing part of it this week, not next.

'Oh, no, it's not,' she'd snapped. 'It's the net result of you trying to put pressure on the owner of our newspaper. If you'd met our editor, Mike Tanner, you might have known that it would be a waste of time,' she added with a grim laugh. 'There's no way he'd ever allow himself to be pushed around. And the outcome of your intervention has been to make him even more determined to publish the article than he was before.'

'You know very well that I loathe the whole idea of this stupid article,' Leo's voice had grated angrily down the phone. But he had not, she'd noticed, denied trying to stop its publication. 'I am not—repeat, *not*—prepared to help you in any way,' he'd continued, his voice tight with rage. 'And, if you *ever* try to contact Fiona again, I'll see to it that you lose your job—if it's the very last thing I do!'

'If I can't write this article, I *will* lose my job,' she'd pointed out bitterly. 'So what have I got to lose? If you absolutely refuse to help me—then I'll just have to go ahead and make it up, won't I?'

Unfortunately, the effect of her last threat had been the sound of Leo swearing violently under his breath, quickly followed by a crash as he'd slammed down the phone.

However, trying to write a work of fiction rather than fact was a lot harder than she'd envisaged. For one thing, Alex knew that she'd have to be very careful not to leave herself open to charges of libel, by either Leo's or Fiona's lawyers. And, although her visit to Hampshire had given her a considerable amount of material, there were still huge gaps in the story which an experienced journalist—such as her editor or, indeed, that awful woman, Imogen Hall-Knightly—would spot in an instant.

Maybe Sophie, if she was in, could help to give her some inspiration. Quickly phoning down to the basement flat in her house, she discovered that her friend had decided to spend the evening in front of the TV and was quite willing to join Alex for a cup of coffee.

'I don't see your problem,' Sophie said later as they sat at the kitchen table. 'You knew Leo and his family eight years ago. So it shouldn't be that hard to write something fairly innocuous to cover the gap up until his engagement to Fiona Bliss.'

Alex shrugged. 'It sounds easy enough,' she admitted glumly. 'But it's a lot harder in practice. In fact,' she added with a sigh, 'if I'd ever thought of writing a work of fiction, trying to make up some romantic nonsense for this article has put me right off the whole idea.'

'You'll think of something,' Sophie laughed. 'In fact, I think that...' She was cut off in mid-flow by the sound of the doorbell, accompanied by a loud drumming of the knocker on the front door. 'Who on earth's that?'

Alex got to her feet. 'I've no idea,' she shrugged. 'I certainly wasn't expecting anyone to call tonight,' she added, making her way out of the kitchen and along the hall to answer the door.

She'd hardly undone the lock before it was shoved wide open and Leo walked past her into the hall.

'It's beginning to snow out there,' he growled, stamping his wet feet on the mat and shrugging off his heavy overcoat, lightly dusted with snow. 'And for goodness' sake stop standing there with your mouth open and get me a strong drink,' he added, tossing the coat at her before striding off down the passage towards the warm, brightly lit kitchen.

Stunned by his sudden arrival, Alex hung up his overcoat before hurrying nervously towards the kitchen, colliding with Sophie in the doorway.

'Don't go!' Alex whispered urgently, grabbing hold of the other girl's arm.

'You must be joking!' her friend muttered, glancing back over her shoulder at the extraordinarily handsome, angry figure pacing up and down the kitchen. 'I take it that's Leo Hamilton?' she hissed, grimacing at Alex's nod of confirmation. 'Rather you than me, kiddo! All I can say is, the very best of luck!' she added with a hollow laugh, before opening the door which led down to the basement flat and quickly disappearing from sight.

CHAPTER SEVEN

'THERE was no need for that girl to take to her heels like a frightened rabbit!' Leo drawled sarcastically as Sophie's hurried footsteps could be heard clattering down the stairs to her own flat.

'"That girl" is my oldest and dearest friend,' Alex snapped. 'Not that it's any business of yours, of course. Which leads me neatly to the question—what in hell are you doing here? And what do you want?'

'Hold it!' Leo gave a snort of caustic laughter. 'I don't think that you're asking the right question, my dear Alex. Please feel free to correct me if I'm wrong,' he added in a hateful, sardonic drawl, 'but, I rather imagined that it was *you* who wanted my help.'

Alex gazed at him in astonishment. 'But…but you were quite adamant about giving me absolutely *no* co-operation, when I phoned you this morning. I mean… you've always simply *hated* the whole idea of the newspaper article.'

'You're quite right—I do,' he agreed curtly. 'However, it didn't take me very long to realise that the end result of your nasty, fertile imagination was likely to be a *much* worse case scenario.'

'Are you really saying…?'

'I'm not saying anything. Not until I've had a strong drink!' he grated, pacing up and down the kitchen floor like a wild beast in its cage.

'Oh…er…right,' she murmured, quickly deciding to

128

ignore any insults. And she'd do well to keep a firm rein
on her loose tongue, Alex warned herself as she took a
glass down from the cupboard and poured him a neat
malt whisky.

There was clearly no point in bothering to speculate
about why this proud, stiff-necked and extremely difficult man had suddenly decided to change his tune. It
was, of course, quite likely that Fiona—or her formidable mother, Ethel Bliss—had finally managed to make
him see sense. They'd probably pointed out that it was
far wiser to co-operate with the newspaper rather than
fight against the publication of what was, after all, a
fairly harmless article.

Whatever the reason for Leo's change of mind, she'd
just have to swallow her pride and be grateful for his
help. Indeed, when she recalled some of the rubbish
she'd been writing earlier this evening, his sudden appearance was beginning to take on the guise of divine
intervention!

Resolutely determined to keep a still tongue in her
head, Alex wondered whether it might be a good idea
to try and drown Leo in honey instead of arguing with
him all the time...? It was certainly worth having a go!

'Well, Leo, I'm not too proud to say that I'm going
to be grateful for any help you can give me,' she told
him meekly. 'I know you're a *very* busy man. And I *do*
understand just how much you actively dislike the idea
of your private life being paraded for public consump-
tion.'

'Hmm...!' he snorted, but there was no doubt in her
mind that some of his anger was beginning to drain
away. Maybe she should have played the 'little woman'
long before now.

'How about coming upstairs, to my study?' she continued. 'We could then try and put together something of which you might, however reluctantly, approve,' she added in a low, soft voice, concentrating on trying to keep up the image of a subservient, weak female. If only Imogen Hall-Knightly could see me now! she thought, struggling to keep her face straight.

He shrugged his broad shoulders. 'Very well,' he sighed, carrying his glass of whisky with him as he followed her down the passage and up the stairs.

Leo's stern expression relaxed a little as he viewed the long, slim legs and trim ankles mounting the stairs in front of him. He had to admit that Alex was looking stunning in that short black skirt and sapphire-blue silk shirt. In fact, the way the thin material clung to her full breasts was more than capable of raising any red-blooded man's temperature! Yet another reason for regretting that he'd given in to that clearly foolish but overwhelming impulse to come here tonight.

While he was definitely no Casanova, as had been reported in the press, he'd certainly known his fair share of women. Which was why he didn't need to be told that having anything more to do with Alex was a recipe for disaster. Ever since he'd first known her, she'd caused nothing but trouble. If he had any sense—and wished to maintain his quiet, well-ordered life, which had suited him so well over the past eight years—he ought to run back down these stairs and leave her house...*right this minute*!

But then, he'd always been an idiot—certainly as far as this girl was concerned, he reminded himself grimly. Although, if she thought she was fooling him with this act she was putting on of a meek and mild, pathetic creature only too anxious to serve her lord and master she was very much mistaken!

Still…he was here now, and it was far too late for him to turn tail and bolt out of the house. Besides, it was surely far better to be in a position to heavily censor anything this damned girl was intending to write than to allow her imagination free rein? And it did at least have the merit of keeping his mother and his uncle off his back until he had the opportunity to sort things out with Fiona.

His mouth tightened ominously as he thought about Ethel Bliss. He certainly had *no* intention of letting that hard, determined woman take charge of *his* life. But he was having the devil's own job in trying to contact Fiona, whose ambitious mother appeared to be making sure that the about-to-be-engaged couple had as little contact with each other as possible.

'Here we are,' Alex trilled as she led the way into her study at the top of the house. 'Now, if you don't mind sitting down in that comfortable chair and giving me the opportunity to take a few notes—principally about what you've been doing during the past eight years—I'm sure we'll be able to get this wrapped up in no time.'

Leo gazed at her steadily for a moment, before going over to sit down in a wide leather chair. 'I think you've forgotten my pipe and slippers.'

'What?'

'Don't get me wrong, Alex.' He gave a low rumble of laughter. 'I definitely appreciate the ''poor helpless female'' and ''sweet little housewife'' performance you're putting on. However, there's really no need to act so out of character.' He grinned. 'Why don't we agree that there's a job to be done—and get on with it?'

'All right…all right!' she snapped, furious at having been rumbled so easily. 'Why don't *you* just shut up and concentrate on your drink while I boot up the computer?'

'Ah, that sounds far more like the Alex Pemberton I know and love,' he murmured sardonically.

'Oh…get lost, you rotten man!' she retorted with a reluctant grin, and sat down at her desk, concentrating on the work in hand.

Just under an hour later, Leo finished reading through the latest draft of her article. 'It's drivel, of course.' He shook his head in weary resignation. 'But I suppose it will have to do.'

'It's hardly likely to win the Pulitzer prize,' Alex agreed with a shrug. 'But, if I'm truthful, I have to admit that it's a lot better than anything I could have written on my own, without your help.'

'Well, for my part, I have to say that I'm surprised how quickly you've managed to produce the damn thing. I fully expected that we'd be at it all night.'

'Thank you for those few kind words.' She grinned, and glanced down at her watch. 'It may not have taken all night, but it's certainly very late, and I expect you're anxious to get home. Which reminds me…' she added with a slightly guilty smile. 'I completely forgot to thank you for returning my car this morning.'

Leo shrugged. 'It was no problem. My local garage are always very helpful.'

Yes—I bet they are! she thought grimly. In fact, it probably costs him a fortune, continually having women's cars towed away from outside his glamorous apartment. And then, quickly realising where her stray thoughts were leading, she swiftly pulled herself together.

'Well, as I've already said, I'm very grateful for your help,' she told him, rising to her feet. 'I'm sure you must be wanting to get home now, especially if it's still snowing,' she added, assuming an efficient, businesslike air, tidying the papers on her desk and turning off the main overhead light as she waited for him to leave.

But the damned man seemed to be in no hurry to go. In fact, if anything, he seemed to be leaning back even further in his chair, clearly quite happy to continue making himself at home.

The soft light from a nearby lamp cast shadows over his handsome features, suddenly seeming to give him a wolf-like, almost saturnine expression, which made her feel suddenly apprehensive and breathless.

'Considering the circumstances, it's turned out to be a very pleasant evening,' he drawled. 'I'm in no hurry to rush outside into the snow.'

'Well, I'm sorry, but I'm afraid you *will* have to face the elements,' she said firmly, determined to keep this highly disturbing relationship as businesslike as possible. 'It's late, and I want to go to bed.'

'What an excellent idea,' he agreed smoothly, rising slowly to his feet.

He didn't move as he stood before her, but all at once the atmosphere of the dimly lit room appeared to become highly charged with an unmistakable, claustrophobic air of sexual tension. Her throat seemed suddenly parched and dry, her heart pounding like a sledge-hammer as she was engulfed by a sudden mad, crazy urge to be clasped tightly in his arms. A totally insane impulse, which she swiftly and ruthlessly crushed without mercy.

'I'm sure you've got better things to do than to hang around here,' she told him coolly, amazed that she was managing to sound so calm and collected as she walked out onto the landing.

But once again, as in his apartment last night, she had badly miscalculated the speed at which this man could move.

One moment there was a good ten feet between them and the next she found herself imprisoned within his arms, her breasts crushed against his hard chest. Almost without thought, she instinctively tried to jerk herself away backwards, the force of the action bringing her spine into jarring contact with the wall behind her.

'You said you wanted to go to bed. Believe me...*so do I*!' he murmured thickly, his arms tightening around her like bands of steel.

'Forget it! You're nothing but bad news,' she cried huskily, desperately twisting to try and free herself from his embrace. Unfortunately, she realised from the darkening gleam in his eyes, and the sudden hardening of the thighs pressing her so closely to the wall, that her struggling body was exciting him.

'Stop...stop this at once, Leo,' she protested breathlessly. 'This is crazy...absolutely insane! Besides, you've no right to do this—not when you're engaged to be married to Fiona Bliss.'

'And if I wasn't going to marry her...? Would you still turn me down?'

'That's not a fair question. The fact is you *are* engaged and...and that's the end of the matter,' she gasped, her trembling figure filled with the familiar sick excitement which she'd felt every time she'd found herself in this man's arms. Staring, mesmerised, up at his mouth, every fibre of her being ached with longing for his warm, sensual lips to be pressed tightly to her own.

The blood seemed to be pounding in her veins, her heart beating so fast that she was certain he must be able to hear it. Oh, Lord! What was happening to her? She couldn't possibly be *still* in love with Leo? Surely not after all these years…?

'Please…please leave me alone,' she muttered helplessly.

'I only wish that I could,' he murmured wryly. 'But it's damn nigh impossible, when I can feel you melting and trembling so invitingly against me; when you say one thing while your body says quite another…' he breathed thickly, lowering his dark head to brush his mouth over her trembling lips, his hands sliding down over her thin silk shirt as he sensually caressed the soft curves of her breasts.

'If you can look me in the eye and tell me—quite truthfully—that you *don't* want me to make love to you, then I'll walk down the stairs and out of your life,' he muttered huskily. 'But I don't think you can tell me that, Alex. Because it's not the truth, is it?'

He was right, she realised with despair. Never in all her life had she wanted anything so badly as she did this man. She couldn't seem to prevent herself from responding to the demanding possession of his lips as he kissed her once more, or the potent urgency of the hard, muscular frame pinning her to the wall. Her hopeless, breathless pleas for him to stop soon became an inaudible moan beneath the melting sweetness and soft seduction of his lips.

'Well…?' he demanded hoarsely.

'Oh, Leo…!' she sighed with helpless resignation.

One part of her mind knew that she would come to bitterly regret her decision, but it seemed she had no choice other than surrender to a force far stronger than anything she had ever known before. Slowly winding her arms up around his neck, she pulled his dark head down towards her.

As their lips met once more, deep shudders shook his tall figure, before he quite suddenly and literally swept her off her feet.

'Where's your bedroom? Hurry up!' he demanded hoarsely of the girl in his arms, who appeared to be in a complete daze. 'If I have to waste time kicking in all the doors—I'll be forced to make love to you here, on the stairs.'

'I thought you could find any woman's bedroom…just like a homing pigeon coming to roost!' she giggled, waving him towards a room at the end of the corridor. It seemed as though, having finally capitulated to this man's overwhelming attraction, all her fears and worries had suddenly disappeared, and she was now feeling quite extraordinarily light-headed, as if high as a kite on champagne.

'Damned cheek! It's high time I taught you some manners,' he growled in rough, unlover-like tones as he strode swiftly down the passage into her room, quickly switching on the light before lightly tossing her down onto the bed.

'Oh, yeah?' she laughed. 'You'll be lucky!'

'You're right—I'm definitely a *very* lucky man,' he agreed quietly, swiftly stripping off his clothes as he gazed down at the glinting blue eyes and soft, trembling lips, the thick mane of fair, sun-bleached hair, and the high, firm breasts of her slim figure.

Even lying dishevelled on the bed, Alex looked totally enchanting as she smiled shyly up at him, and Leo knew that he'd completely and utterly lost all sense and caution. There was no way he could hope to exert control over his emotions, which were now adamantly refusing to respond to the tight rein he'd struggled to hold them with during the past few days.

'Leo...?' she whispered, suddenly feeling nervous, despite the heady stream of almost overpowering excitement flowing through her veins as he joined her on the bed. 'Are you quite sure that this is a good idea...?'

'Oh, yes. After waiting eight long years, I'm now quite...*quite* sure!' he murmured huskily as he pulled her towards him, burying his face in her thick mane of sweet-smelling fair hair.

Alex felt as if she was in a trance, savouring the heat of his body, through the thin layer of her silk shirt and the masculine, musky scent of his cologne as his lips moved softly over her forehead, pressing warm kisses on her eyelids, before trailing down to delicately touch a corner of her lips.

With tantalising slowness he explored her soft mouth with gentle, sensual kisses that set the blood rushing through her veins. His moist, firm lips gradually became more insistent, his kiss deepening as he sensuously and erotically explored the inner softness of her mouth. She felt as if she was drowning, drifting way out of her depth, as she buried her fingers convulsively in his dark hair, dizzily responding to the fast, irregular beating of his heart so close to her own, the increasingly urgent hunger in his lips.

'*My sweet, lovely Alex...*' he breathed thickly, his hands moving over the swelling curves of her breasts and thighs before swiftly undoing the buttons of her silk blouse. She trembled with pleasure at the touch of his warm fingers on her flesh, frenzied shivers of excitement gripping her stomach as she felt the moist heat of his lips kissing the deep cleft between her soft breasts.

Locked in passion, she hardly noticed his slow removal of her clothes, only conscious of responding with voluptuous delight as his lips traced their passing with lingering, sensual pleasure. There was no part of her that did not respond to him, her whole being vibrating in response to the highly erotic, electrifying sensations engendered by his mouth and hands as they caressed every inch of her soft flesh.

'Oh, God—*Leo*...!' she gasped, her body suddenly turned to molten fire, burning and craving his possession as she arched wantonly against his hard, muscular form, her total abandonment inciting his own arousal as she sobbed his name in a mindless refrain, before the intense, tingling excitement which had been filling her body suddenly exploded deep within her.

A deep, husky growl was torn from his throat as he quickly parted her thighs, her sweet moistness enveloping his fiercely thrusting manhood. Beneath the urgently propulsive, rhythmic force of his strong body, she became a wild creature that matched him in the elemental, wildly primitive storm of passion that totally possessed them both, pleasure exploding yet again and again inside her, until, all passion spent, she floated slowly back down to earth within the warmth and comfort of his strong embrace.

Later, as they lay quietly entwined together, with her head cradled on his arm and his lips buried in her fragrant fair hair, Alex thought that she couldn't ever remember having been so happy. Or so emotionally fulfilled. Drowsily, almost on the verge of sleep, a name suddenly began flashing urgently in her weary brain.

Oh, Lord—*Fiona*! And, even as she realised that they *must* talk about his engagement to the other girl, she suddenly recalled Fiona's words about preferring horses to most human beings, that the exhilaration of riding over jumps across country was better than anything...far better than sex. And she remembered just how astonished she'd been to learn that Leo *wasn't* particularly good in bed.

But...but that *had* to be nonsense! She wasn't an expert on the subject, of course. But Alex had absolutely no doubt that Leo was a truly superb lover. So why...why had Fiona been so dismissive? It simply didn't make sense...

The slight, puzzled shrug of her slim shoulders roused Leo, whose arms tightened about her. As his lips trailed slowly down over the long line of her neck to taste the sweetness of her breasts, she heard him give a dry grunt of amusement.

'God knows what you do to me, my darling, but it seems I can't keep my hands off you,' he murmured, teasing her body with his fingertips in a tantalising, feather-like touch that left her breathless with desire.

'Leo...!' she gasped helplessly a few moments later. 'No, really...there are things we must talk about.'

'Yes, I know,' he sighed, drawing her firmly back within his arms. 'I've never really apologised to you for what happened during that disastrous night in Tuscany, have I? I think I was too ashamed...too distressed...'

'No, I didn't mean...I wasn't thinking of Italy,' she muttered quickly. 'I meant...' But she was prevented from saying any more as his lips possessed hers in a quick kiss.

'They say confession is good for the soul, and it's time I told you the truth,' he murmured as his mouth left hers, and he pulled her closer to him as he lay back on the pillows.

'I was twenty-three at the time, and had my own circle of friends. So I've never been able to understand exactly *why* I began taking notice of the tall, slim and gawky sixteen-year-old who'd come out to stay with my family that summer.'

He was silent for a moment before she felt him shake his head. 'I've never been able to find a rational explanation for why I first became mildly interested, and then highly intrigued, to discover what made that young girl tick. It's only now, with hindsight, that I realise that there must have been a very strong, fierce bond of sexual attraction, which I was just too young and callow to understand at the time. And it's not surprising that I was so blind and unable to understand my own emotions...'

His shoulders shook with wry amusement. 'Because your appearance was certainly *very* different from that of my usual girlfriends.'

'I did look a fright, didn't I?' she sighed.

'Yes, my darling, I'm afraid you did,' he agreed with a low rumble of laughter, and leaned over to kiss her once again.

'But, once I'd looked past that punk, strangely aggressive exterior, I became...well, possibly ''captivated'' is the right word to describe my feelings for a girl who, despite all her problems—especially with my mother!—refused to sink beneath a sea of troubles. In fact, I became fascinated by the way in which you managed to stand up and hold your own in a very difficult situation.'

This was such a different view from how she'd seen herself at the time, that Alex had difficulty in matching the two portraits of herself. 'But I was absolutely terrified of you all,' she murmured. 'And though, of course, I'd fallen madly in love with you—just the sort of mad crush that I suppose is normal for a young girl—I think I found you, Leo, the most frightening of all.'

'Well, I know that I certainly didn't behave very well. On the one hand, the difference in our age meant that I normally wouldn't have been seen dead taking any notice of such a young girl. But, on the other hand, I couldn't seem to leave you alone. And then...' He gave a deep sigh. 'Then my mother proceeded to go completely off the rails.'

He gave another, heavy sigh. 'I love my mother, of course, but there's no way I can find any excuse for her behaviour towards you. When I returned to the villa that day, and found out what had been going on in my absence, I nearly had a blue fit. But, although I got you out of jail as fast as I possibly could, the damage had been done.

'And who could blame you for hating and loathing every single member of my family?' he said bleakly. 'It was because I wanted to offer some restitution, some comfort to a girl who'd been treated so disgracefully, that I came to your room that night. And, well...you know the rest. To put it bluntly, Alex, once I'd put my arms around you—I instantly lost all control of the situation. And the fact that I finally, at the very last minute, managed to pull myself together and get a grip on life hardly reflects any credit on my behaviour at the time.'

'I thought…I thought you found me disgusting. I was so sure that…'

'Absolutely not!' he assured her quickly. 'I was disgusted with *myself*! I was overcome with horror that I could so easily have taken the innocence of a young girl who'd not only been a guest in my stepfather's house, but also shamefully treated by my mother. Believe me,' he added with a shaky, mirthless laugh, 'I've *never* been so near to slitting my own throat as I was later that night. Which is why I left the villa so early the next morning. I've no excuse for vanishing in the way I did. I was so full of shame and self-loathing that I just wanted to put as much distance between us as possible.'

'I do understand, Leo,' she told him gently, thankful to be released from the burden which had lain so heavily on her all these years.

'No, I don't think you do,' he said slowly, the sadness in his voice almost wringing her heart. 'I think I said earlier that this was a confession—and so it is. Because, although I returned eventually to the villa, ready to face any and all recriminations which you might throw at my head—and fully aware that I owed you a deep apology— it was to discover that you had returned to England. And I have to say, although it hurts me to do so, that I took the weak and cowardly way out of the situation by doing absolutely nothing.

'I *could* have made an effort to contact you, once I'd returned to England, after the holiday. And there have been plenty of opportunities, during the past eight years, when it would have been possible to locate your whereabouts and to offer my sincere if belated apologies for what had happened in Italy. But, as we both know, I did none of those things. I merely got on with my life and conveniently forgot the hurt I'd caused you. And then, eight years later, you suddenly appear in my office. *My God...!* I can tell you that I nearly had a heart attack when you told me your name!'

'Oh, darling, *please* don't torture yourself like this,' she cried. 'Everything that's happened is now well in the past. Surely it's only the here and now that matters?'

'My sweet, lovely Alex—you're far more generous than I deserve,' he groaned huskily, urgently drawing her soft body close to him, covering her face with feather-like kisses before his lips claimed hers with possessive hunger.

'For heaven's sake, Leo!' she gasped a few moments later. 'I really...I really do have to talk to you because...'

'No, I don't think so...not *just* at the moment,' he murmured thickly, the ensuing silence only disturbed by their softly whispered endearments as once again he made love to her with a tender passion and gentle, leisured delight, ravishing her senses until she was reduced to mindless ecstasy as he brought them both to the exquisite satisfaction of mutual fulfilment.

The next thing Alex knew, she was being jerked sharply awake by the loud, strident ringing of her alarm clock.

Sitting up startled in bed, she only just noticed that Leo was no longer lying beside her when the bedroom door opened and he came into the room, fully dressed, carrying a cup and saucer.

'I thought I'd bring you a cup of tea, just before I have to rush off,' he said, placing it down on her bedside table. 'I'm sorry that I have to dash, but I've got an urgent meeting at the bank first thing this morning.'

'But we haven't talked…I mean, we haven't discussed the problem of Fiona. I feel really terrible, and I'm sure that…'

'That's no problem. It won't be long before I've got the whole business sorted out. I'll be in touch, and give you a ring as soon as possible,' he added, glancing quickly down at his watch before hurrying back across the room, and blowing her a kiss as he quickly closed the door behind him.

And that was the last she'd seen of the double-crossing, two-timing *rat fink*! Alex told herself grimly, sitting downstairs in the kitchen and staring dismally into her early morning cup of tea exactly one week later.

Well, they always said that there was one fool born every minute—and this time it had *definitely* been her! What a sucker. Talk about pathetic! How he must have laughed, after spinning that web of seduction, to find how easily she'd dropped into his hands, just like a ripe plum.

'Oh, boy! Were you an idiot—or what?' she muttered. But, despite knowing it was pointless to keep rubbing salt into her wounds, she still couldn't come to terms with the fact that, once again, Leo seemed to have succeeded in messing up her life.

An outsider, or some of her female friends with slightly looser morals than her own, might think she was being ultra-, super-sensitive about the whole affair. And, yes, maybe if Leo hadn't left her feeling so totally devastated eight years ago, she might have tried and made an effort to assume a casual, sophisticated attitude to what, she now realised, was merely a one-night stand.

But she still carried the scars of what had happened

in Italy all those years ago. Discovering that her childish infatuation had grown and matured into an adult emotion, and that she was now deeply in love with Leo, made the humiliating position in which she now found herself almost unendurable. Because, if he *really* cared for her—and, following his 'confession' after they'd made love, she'd foolishly assumed that he did—Leo would have made at least a serious effort to contact her over the last seven days.

Well…to give the devil his due, there hadn't been a complete and utter silence, she reminded herself grimly. There had been that strange and highly unsatisfactory phone call which she'd received in the newspaper office last Monday afternoon.

Unfortunately, she'd been frantically typing up her interview of earlier that day with the wife of a well-known TV personality, who'd just discovered that her husband was intending to trade her in for a young, blonde bimbo. And, since Mike Tanner was anxious to scoop the rest of Fleet Street with the story, Alex had a deadline hanging over her like the sword of Damocles.

So it had obviously *not* been the best time for her to take a call from Leo, who'd been using what appeared to be a highly defective mobile phone.

In fact, it had been some moments before she'd realised exactly who was on the line, the noisy static and barely audible voice making any sensible conversation almost impossible.

'Where on earth are you…? What…? For heaven's sake, speak up!' she yelled down the phone.

'There's no need to shout…hear you quite plainly,' Leo's whispering, rippling voice was barely audible, as if he was speaking from somewhere at the bottom of the ocean.

'Well, I can hardly hear you,' she muttered, one eye on the clock as she quickly tucked the phone under her chin, freeing her hands to type a quick alteration to her story on the screen in front of her. 'Look—give me your number, and I'll ring you back.'

Leo's tinny whisper seemed to come and go in waves, as if she was holding a sea-shell to her ear. 'Not possible…Fiona…business…can't make the ball on Thursday…'

'Oh, great! That's all I need,' Alex groaned. 'Please… Oh, *please* don't do this to me, Leo,' she begged, ashamed and humiliated to find herself pleading with the man—who hadn't even bothered to be in touch with her after their lovemaking five days ago—purely in an effort to save her job.

'Sorry…good reasons why…Fiona, you see…'

'No, I *don't* see!' she shouted, frustrated to hear only an empty silence, before there was a click and the sound of a dialling tone indicating that the call had been terminated.

And that had been that. No message; no further phone calls, and no response from either Leo or his fiancée to her article in the *Chronicle*'s Saturday magazine supplement.

As it had turned out, her editor's idea of turning the magazine completely over to the subject of romance had not only been a great success with their readers, but also significantly increased the *Chronicle*'s sales figures. Those two facts—together with Imogen Hall-Knightly's fury at being proved wrong—had kept Mike Tanner in high good humour for some time.

As far as her own piece was concerned, Alex had been really pleased to hear from the two other couples, who'd all expressed their pleasure at the way their stories had been written. So why should she care if there had been nothing but a deathly silence from both Leo and Fiona Bliss?

But despite what she thought and said, and her anger at what she could only think of as the ultimate betrayal, there seemed nothing she could do to assuage the deep, searing humiliation of knowing that she'd made such a fool of herself. Or the fact that there had hardly been one moment of the last seven days and nights when she hadn't been racked with misery and pain.

The hope that by burying herself in work she might somehow alleviate the torment and the intense, aching need to feel the caress of his hands on her body once again had been of no use whatsoever. In fact, her temper had been on such a short fuse these last few days that she could well be in danger of losing her job. Snapping at Mike Tanner yesterday had been a great mistake. One more slip-up like that, and she could well get the sack.

Of course, what was really making her feel excessively tired and jumpy was the fact that the St Valentine's Ball was being held tonight. Sheer, naked pride had prevented her from lifting the phone and calling Leo to beg him to reconsider his decision. And, quite honestly, she'd almost got to the point where she didn't give a toss. The article might look a bit weird, accompanied only by pictures of two couples instead of three. But so what? Quite frankly she was so utterly fed up with the whole rotten idea of this St Valentine's Day caper that she'd almost got to the point of not caring whether she lost her job as well.

Maybe she wasn't really cut out for journalism. Possibly her choice of career had all been a ghastly mistake, and she'd be happier doing something quite different. Like becoming an air hostess, or a holiday courier. Both those jobs would at least have the virtue of getting her out of the country and well away from Leo, she was telling herself grimly when she heard a loud knocking on the door.

Quickly checking that the chain was in place—because, if by some chance it *was* Leo, she'd no intention of allowing him to get even one toenail over the threshold—she gingerly inched the front door open.

'Oh, hello Susan,' she said, surprised to see the tax inspector's fiancée standing on her doorstep. 'I'm sorry, I haven't got dressed yet,' she added, gesturing at her long dressing gown and slippers. 'I was just having a cup of tea in the kitchen; would you like to join me?'

'Oh, yes…yes, I would,' Susan muttered, before suddenly bursting into tears. 'Nigel and I had the most terrible row last night,' she wailed as Alex put her arm around the girl's shoulders, and drew her gently into the house. 'We've broken off our engagement. And…and I said…that I never, *ever* wanted to see him again!'

CHAPTER EIGHT

'OH, SUSAN—I'm *so* sorry,' Alex murmured, immediately forgetting her own problems as she led the sobbing girl down the hall towards the kitchen.

'Now, I'm sure this is all just engagement nerves. But why don't you take off your coat, sit down and tell me all about it?'

'I simply couldn't believe it when Nigel was *so* rude to Mummy,' Susan sobbed some time later, having given Alex a blow by blow account of exactly how, and why, she and her fiancé had broken off their engagement. 'Of course, she really shouldn't have said all those nasty things, so I suppose it wasn't *all* his fault.'

'No, well...' Alex murmured, deciding that this was probably the perfect moment to brew a strong cup of coffee.

Having listened patiently for the last half hour while Susan had poured her heart out, Alex had no trouble in coming to the conclusion that the fault lay fairly and squarely with Susan's mother.

From the sound of it, the woman seemed to be an absolute dragon. Definitely a twin soul to Ethel Bliss! And with his mother-in-law to be apparently determined to take charge of every aspect of their future life, it was no wonder that Nigel had finally decided that he'd had enough. Poor Susan was obviously well aware of where the true blame lay. Only family loyalty to her own mother seemed to be preventing her from acknowledging the fact.

'I really don't want to be a problem,' the other girl said as Alex placed a cup of coffee in front of her. 'It's just...well, we all got on so well when you came to interview us for your article. Which was why I felt I *must* tell you, in person, the reason why Nigel and I won't be going to the St Valentine's Ball tonight,' she said sorrowfully, the tears trickling down her cheeks once again.

'It was nice of you to come to see me. But there's no need to worry about missing the ball,' Alex told her firmly. 'It's hardly the end of the world, you know!'

Since Leo and Fiona were obviously not going to be turning up at the dance, the fact that Nigel and Susan couldn't make it either didn't really seem to matter. However, since they were both such nice people, and ideally suited for one another, she really must try and do her best to help them get back together again.

'If you don't mind, I'm just going to nip upstairs and put on some clothes,' Alex told the tearful girl. 'I won't be a moment, so drink your coffee, blow your nose— and try to calm down!'

'I'll do my best.' Susan gave her a wobbly grin. 'Thank you so much. You've been very kind.'

Alex laughed. 'Just regard it as all part of the normal *Chronicle* service,' she grinned, and quickly whisked herself upstairs.

Swiftly pulling on a burgundy cashmere polo-necked sweater over matching slim woollen trousers, Alex sat on the edge of the bed and pulled the phone towards her. Dialling through to Nigel's office, she was relieved when he answered after only a few rings. Briefly explaining why she was phoning, Alex listened as patiently as she could to his side of the story.

'It's all right, Nigel, you don't have to convince *me*,' she told him. 'The point is—and it's the *only* thing that really matters—do you love Susan? And if so, surely you have to ask yourself the question—who are you *actually* intending to marry? Susan or her mother?'

A wide grin spread over Alex's face as Nigel gave vent to his feelings about his future mother-in-law. Holding the phone well away from her ear, she waited until the sorely tried man finally began to run out of steam.

'Come on, Nigel...!' she laughed as he continued to splutter down the other end of the phone. 'Susan is absolutely crazy about you—so this is clearly no time for British reserve. This is a time for positive action, right? So, how about if I keep Susan here with me for the rest of today—well away from her dear mother!—and we'll join you at the hotel tonight at eight o'clock. OK?'

Feeling pleased with herself, Alex ran back downstairs. 'Well, that's sorted out most of your problems, Susan,' she announced as she entered the kitchen, only to discover her friend Sophie sitting at the kitchen table listening to her visitor's sad story.

'It sounds as though Nigel needs a good dose of gumption!' Sophie announced as Alex joined them.

'Oh, no, he doesn't,' Alex retorted firmly. 'Of course, it's up to Susan. But I've just been talking to Nigel, who is full to the brim with gumption—and has every intention of attending the ball tonight!'

She turned to the girl whose tearful face was now suddenly wreathed in an ecstatically happy smile. 'As far as I can see, there's no need for you to go home. All you'll have to do is spend the day here, with us, and we can all go off to the ball together. So how about it?'

'I'd really love to,' Susan assured her, obviously quite happy about not having to face her mother any sooner than she had to. 'But…but my dress and things are still at home. And I really don't think I can face any more rows, or…'

'That's no problem,' Alex assured her swiftly. 'I made a stupid bet with Sophie the other day. And, since I lost the wager, she's going to be wearing my best ball gown. Which means that I've got to go out and buy myself something to wear. So, we'll just look around for a dress for you as well.'

'Oh, I couldn't possibly…I mean, it would cost far too much, and…'

'The *Chronicle* will be quite happy to pay the bill,' Alex told her firmly, refusing to feel guilty about telling such a whopping lie.

As she knew, only too well, there was no way that her editor would agree to pick up the tab for such frippery. However, thanks to her grandmother's fortune, money had always been the very least of Alex's problems. So, why not let Susan believe that a large organisation, such as the *Chronicle*, was paying for the dress, when she might well refuse to let Alex do so? She was always careful not to flaunt the fact that she was very wealthy. But the cost of a new ball gown would be a mere drop in the ocean, as far as the Rothstein fortune was concerned.

Later that afternoon, in the heart of Mayfair, Eleanor Lucas was pouring her son a cup of tea. 'Or would you rather have coffee, dear?'

Leo shook his head. 'No, tea's fine. I've already had enough coffee on the plane to keep me wide awake for a week.'

'Well, I'm so pleased to hear that you've agreed to come to the ball. I really do welcome your support, you know,' she murmured, well aware that being forced to attend her annual charity bash was definitely not her son's idea of having a good time.

Handing him a slice of fruitcake, Eleanor suddenly recalled the old rhyming adage: a daughter's a daughter for all of her life—a son's a son till he takes him a wife. How very true! she thought with an inward sigh.

She hadn't yet met his fiancée, but she'd heard that Fiona was a very pretty girl. However, the prospect of having to share her future grandchildren with Ethel Bliss was honestly more than she could bear to contemplate.

There were plenty of people who might think that she, herself, wasn't exactly a pushover. But Eleanor knew that she simply wasn't in the same league as Fiona's mother! That pushy woman, who was as hard as nails— and virtually unstoppable once she'd got her teeth into something—would soon be running Fiona and Leo's lives for them, whether they liked it or not.

Of course, it wasn't easy to push her dear son around, as she knew to her cost. But she doubted that even *his* hard, tough personality would be able to cope with the unrelenting force of his future mother-in-law.

'Right, I must be off,' Leo said, rising to his feet and quickly finishing his cup of tea. 'I only just popped in to say hello. By the way,' he added casually, 'I don't suppose you've heard anything from Fiona…?'

'No, dear.' She shook her head. 'Although, I believe she did ring a few days ago, wanting to talk to you. One of the servants took the call, and since I naturally assumed that she'd contact you at your apartment, I—'

'Did she leave a number where I can reach her?' he demanded urgently.

Eleanor shrugged. 'She might have. If so, it'll be on the notepad by the phone, in the hall.'

A moment or two later, Leo was swiftly dialling a number.

'Ah, Fiona—at last! I've been trying to get in touch with you for the last few days... Yes, yes, that's no problem... Yes, I'm quite certain. You're right. I know that we're both going to be very happy. Goodbye, darling—and don't forget to give my love to your dear mother!' he added with a laugh, before putting down the phone.

'Cheers, everyone—here's to us!' Alex called out, smiling as she raised her champagne glass to salute her guests, who were excitedly chatting to each other in the large sitting room.

'Well, I must say that I think you've done Susan proud,' Sophie said as she came over to the small side table to replenish her glass. 'Let's hope that Nigel really *does* turn up at the ball tonight.'

'I daren't even *think* about what would happen if he didn't,' Alex agreed fervently, her friend having accurately voiced her own fears. 'Susan does look terrific, doesn't she?'

'Absolutely stunning,' Sophie agreed as they both stared at the girl standing across the room.

Having only met Susan during the course of writing her article, Alex hadn't been at all sure how she and the other girl would get on together during the course of the

long day. But she needn't have worried. Right from the
moment they'd left the house, intent on a mad spending
spree, they'd both had a really great time.

With London's King's Road full of dress shops and
exclusive boutiques, it hadn't been long before they'd
found the perfect ball gown to complement Susan's pale
skin and auburn hair.

It had clearly been a great choice, Alex thought now,
gazing at the emerald-green satin dress, with its tight
bodice emphasising Susan's tiny waist and sweeping out
into a full, gathered skirt. With matching shoes and small
evening purse completing her ensemble, she looked really *so* pretty that Alex was certain that Nigel had only
to take one glance at his fiancée, before he fell more
madly in love with her than ever.

In fact, Alex thought as she glanced around the room,
she was really highly delighted at the effort everyone
had made to look so glamorous for the ball tonight.

While Dave seemed slightly uncomfortable, occasion-
ally running a finger around the collar of his white evening shirt and clearly unaccustomed to wearing a dinner
jacket, his girlfriend Kelly had really pulled out all the
stops. The white-gold hair piled up in an intricate chi-
gnon at the top of her head might have been expected
from someone who owned a hairdressing salon, however, the long, figure-hugging plain black crêpe dress
had been an inspired choice. Wearing no jewellery but
a small pair of gold earrings, Kelly looked a million
dollars.

'Don't they look great together?' she muttered to
Sophie as they stared at the plumber and his girlfriend.

'Mmm...' her friend agreed. 'And, if I may say so,
you don't look too bad yourself, kiddo!' she added, roll-

ing her eyes dramatically, before crossing the room to replenish the others' glasses.

Nor do you, Alex thought, quickly deciding to make Sophie a permanent gift of the long gold sheath dress. Quite why she'd ever thought of it as her 'best' dress, she had no idea. Because it obviously suited the other girl's dark colouring far better than it had ever done her own.

However, she had *very* strong doubts about her new ball gown. In fact, she was definitely beginning to think that she'd made a great mistake in allowing Susan's encouragement to override her own good sense on their shopping trip earlier today.

As soon as they'd set eyes on the vivid crimson satin dress with its *very* low-cut, heart-shaped strapless bodice, Susan had declared that it would be absolutely perfect for a St Valentine's Day Ball.

And maybe she had a point. But Alex couldn't get rid of the sneaking suspicion that she now bore a very strong resemblance to Jessica Rabbit—the heroine of a wildly popular film which mixed cartoon characters with real actors.

Her thoughts were interrupted by a loud ringing of the doorbell, and she quickly gathered up her guests, shepherding them out of the house and into the ultra-glamorous stretch limousine which she had hired to take them to the ball.

'Well…I reckon that this has to be the *only* way to travel!' Dave exclaimed as they arrived outside the large London hotel. 'Come on, ladies—let's hit the big time!' he added, giving a regal, lordly nod of thanks to the chauffeur and following the rest of the party up the steps and through the wide revolving door.

'Relax—stay cool!' Alex murmured to Susan, who was hanging nervously back and gazing with frightened eyes at the large foyer crowded with guests. 'I'm quite sure that Nigel *will* turn up. And, believe me, he's going to think you look fantastic.'

'Oh, I do hope so,' the other girl muttered nervously.

However, it very soon became clear that she needn't have worried. Because, just as they were making their way towards the cloakroom to get rid of their overcoats and warm wraps, Alex spied the thin, fair-haired figure of Nigel, pushing his way through the crowd towards them.

'I think "gobsmacked" is the right word!' Sophie laughed as they watched Nigel staring transfixed down at his fiancée, as if gazing at a divine vision. In fact, it almost brought a tear to Alex's eyes to see the tender way in which he gently raised her hand to his lips, before grinning proudly as he led Susan away into the ballroom.

'I don't think that you'll see very much more of them tonight! I've never seen such a case of love's young dream,' Sophie muttered, a distinct note of envy in her voice.

'What about your date?' Alex asked.

Her friend shrugged. 'He's bound to be around here somewhere. Oh, yes, there he is.' She waved to a tall, handsome man across the room. 'See you later, OK?'

Alex nodded as Dave and Kelly joined her.

'This is really great!' Dave said enthusiastically. 'We think we'll just go off, if that's all right?'

'Fine,' Alex told him. 'I'm just going to track down our photographer, and then I think we'll take most of the pictures as soon as possible. Which will mean you can then spend the rest of the evening enjoying your-selves.'

'That's a good idea,' Kelly agreed with a grin. 'Es-pecially as I'm not sure just how long this hairdo of mine is going to stay up in one piece!'

By the time Alex met up with Sid Reilly, most of the couples attending the dance had drifted away from the foyer and into the ballroom. It now looked almost certain that Leo and Fiona were not going to turn up.

What's new? she asked herself grimly, trying to ig-nore the load of heavy depression settling on her bare shoulders. After all, she'd always known that Leo would do his very best to wriggle out of attending this func-tion—even if the ball was organised by his mother.

'Now, are you sure that you know which are the right couples?' she asked Sid. 'It would be a disaster if you took pictures of the wrong ones!'

'Yeah. There won't be any problem,' he assured her. 'Although I must say that *you're* looking very tasty, Alex. Very tasty, indeed!' he added with a wolfish leer. 'How that dress of yours manages to defy the laws of gravity beats me!'

'Get lost, Sid! Kindly remember that you've a job to do.' She grinned, having worked with the photographer before, and being well used to his banter. All the same…his words had accurately reflected her own doubts about the dress she was wearing. If her grand-mother, for instance, had ever seen her in such a low-cut gown—she'd have had raving hysterics!

'Talking of doing my job,' Sid was saying, 'I thought Mike said that there were supposed to be *three* pairs of lovebirds here tonight. Do I take it that one pair has flown away?'

'Something like that,' she agreed, and was just explaining that, despite all her best efforts, the upper-class couple hadn't bothered to turn up, when she felt her arm being firmly grasped by a tall figure standing behind her.

'*Leo...!*' she gasped as he spun her around to face him.

All the carefully prepared, crushing remarks which she'd been practising for the past week seemed to have deserted her as she gazed up into the gleaming green eyes beneath their heavy eyelids.

'I...er...I was quite certain that you weren't going to turn up,' she muttered lamely as she desperately tried to pull herself together.

'Oh, ye of little faith,' he drawled coolly, before adding with a grin, 'I couldn't possibly be expected to miss seeing you in that quite disgracefully sexy dress, could I?'

'But...but where's Fiona?' Alex asked, gazing quickly about the foyer as she tried to spot the other girl's small, slight, dark figure.

As much as she'd like to tell the foul man *exactly* what he could do with himself, Alex suddenly realised that she couldn't. Or, at least, not just at the moment.

Unfortunately, she had no alternative but to face the harsh facts of life: both she and Sid still had a job to do. It was only after the photographer had taken his pictures of the happy couples that she'd be able to have a blazing row with Leo—something she'd been looking forward to for the past week. And, with any luck, she told herself viciously, cut him *well* down to size!

''Ere. Isn't this one of them missing aristos, then?' Sid enquired, quickly snapping off a picture of Leo with his arm still about Alex's waist.

'Yes, he is.'

'No, I'm not.'

Both Alex and Leo answered together at once.

'Suit yourselves!' Sid shrugged, before ambling off to photograph the other two couples.

'So—where *is* Fiona?' Alex enquired bleakly, moving adroitly away from his tall figure. 'If *you've* actually bothered to turn up, I don't suppose your girlfriend can be far behind.'

'Well, that's where you're quite wrong,' Leo told her, his dark brows lowering as he frowned down at the tight, almost aggressive expression on Alex's lovely face. 'Look, we've got to have a good, long talk,' he added, taking her arm and steering her across the foyer, away from the ballroom towards a quiet bar.

'The thing is, Fiona couldn't make it here tonight. I'll explain exactly why, of course, but I'm going to have to ask you to... Oh, Lord—that's torn it!'

Startled to hear him mutter a quick oath under his breath, Alex's gaze followed his to see a large, imperious lady bearing down on them. She would have recognised that huge beaky nose anywhere! It *had* to be Leo's mother, Eleanor Lucas!

'Hello, darling!' the woman called out while still some six feet away, her voice booming like a foghorn and echoing off the walls of the large foyer. 'How lovely to meet dear Fiona at last!'

Quickly clasping Alex's arm in an iron grip, Leo hissed out of the side of his mouth, 'For God's sake— keep your mouth shut. Fiona couldn't make it tonight. So just agree to everything I say, OK?'

'What...?' Alex gazed up at him in bewilderment.

'My dear, I'm so glad you were able to come to the

ball.' Eleanor was braying with a wide, toothy grin, clearly not recognising the girl she'd once known eight years ago. 'And how is your mother? It seems simply ages since I've seen dear Ethel,' the older woman added, with a completely false smile pinned to her lips.

'Ethel and George were sorry they couldn't be here tonight,' Leo was saying coolly, when Alex suddenly decided *she'd had it*!

She didn't know what game these awful people thought they were playing—but she certainly had no intention of letting Leo make a fool of her yet again! Why on earth should she have to pretend to be Fiona Bliss? The whole idea was *ridiculous*!

On the other hand…why not? Goodness knows, she had a long overdue score to settle with ghastly Eleanor Lucas. What the heck? She might as well enjoy herself—and cause as much trouble as possible.

'I'm *so* sorry Mummy isn't here,' Alex simpered, trying her best to mimic Fiona's breathless, small voice. 'But, as she said, there's no way she could bring herself to attend such a boring, low-class sort of function—full of the *hoi polloi* and general riff-raff of London.'

'Oh, really…?' Eleanor's lips tightened into an ominously thin line.

'Mmm…' Alex nodded happily, giving the older woman a beaming smile while Leo's figure suddenly stiffened; he frowned down at the girl beside him, as if not entirely sure that he'd heard her correctly.

'Which is why Mummy has decided to organise her *own* St Valentine's ball next year,' Alex prattled on, accurately placing her poisoned darts where she knew they would cause the most damage. 'And, of course, it's sure to be a *big* success, because most of her friends and acquaintances have already promised to buy lots of tickets.'

'Oh, *really*…? That's *very* interesting!' Eleanor snapped angrily, her cheeks suddenly purple with rage at the thought of Ethel Bliss intending to take over *her* role as organiser of the best charity ball in London. 'It seems I must have a word or two with your *dear* mother, doesn't it?' she added grimly.

Right! That should take care of both Eleanor *and* Fiona's mother, Alex told herself gleefully, feeling that she ought to be congratulated for scoring two bull's-eyes at one and the same time.

'Stop this—at once!' Leo hissed out of the corner of his mouth, his fingers tightening threateningly on her arm.

'Of course, Mummy's absolutely mad about my *darling,* Leo,' Alex continued, ignoring the dangerous glint of anger in his eyes as she gave him an adoring, simpering smile.

'I'm *such* a lucky girl!' she continued quickly, not giving Leo a chance to say anything as she turned back to flash Eleanor yet another hundred-megawatt smile. 'Especially when I think of all those thousands of really, *really* glamorous women who've been in and out of his bedroom over the past few years!'

'For God's sake!' Leo exploded.

His mother gave an anxious, nervous laugh, quickly glancing around the foyer to make sure that no one else—especially any reporters!—had heard the artless prattle of this very beautiful but obviously dim-witted girl. She'd always known, of course, that her handsome son was…er…very attractive to the opposite sex. But he couldn't possibly… Not *that* number of women, surely?

'Oh, yes! Mummy says that he's a *real* tiger between the sheets!' Alex continued, positively drunk on the heady fumes of revenge.

Ignoring both Leo's fury and the harsh pain of his iron fingers suddenly biting deep into her arm, she added in a light, artless voice, *'Darling* Leo has said that I mustn't expect him to give up *all* his girlfriends when we're married because it would be asking *far* too much. But Mummy says that the threat of a loud, noisy and very acrimonious divorce case will soon sort him out. What do you think?'

Eleanor gasped, clasping a hand to her bosom and turning her horrified gaze on her son, quite sure that she was about to have a heart attack any minute.

But he, suddenly breaking out of his equally horrified trance, was now striding swiftly away towards the ballroom, determinedly dragging his 'fiancée' behind him.

'And just *what* did you think you were doing with that quite *disgusting*, totally slanderous performance?' he ground out through clenched teeth, marching onto the dance floor and pulling her roughly into his arms.

'I was just enjoying myself at your expense, *you rat*!' she retorted, raising her voice to be heard over the music. 'After all, it was *your* idea to pretend that I was Fiona Bliss. And where *is* your dear fiancée, anyway?'

'You can leave Fiona out of this,' he hissed furiously, and moved adroitly to avoid another couple on the crowded floor. 'Because she had absolutely nothing to do with that…that *horrific* exhibition you've just put on. Goodness knows the ideas you've now put into my mother's head!' he raged, practically grinding his teeth with fury.

'I'm not going to suffer a bleeding heart about *that*,'

Alex retorted. 'Besides, maybe it's about time that Eleanor learned just what a Casanova her son really is. You really do believe in the adage "love 'em and leave 'em", don't you?' she added with a shrill, high-pitched laugh.

'What the hell are you talking about?'

'I'm talking about the fact that it's a week since I last saw you and you haven't even bothered to try and contact me. Other than a brief call—which didn't make any sense at all—from somewhere that sounded like the bottom of the sea. So, it looks as if I was just another notch on your bedpost, doesn't it?' she ground out, desperately wishing that there were enough room on the dance floor for her to be able to take a hefty swing and give him a punishing kick on the shins.

'You're determined to think ill of me, aren't you?' he demanded angrily.

'Yes, I damn well am!' she snapped, just getting ready to give him yet another piece of her mind when she found herself jerked hard up against his chest, his arms closing tightly about her slim figure as his mouth ruthlessly crushed hers in a furiously angry kiss.

There were, of course, many other dancers on the floor engaged in romantic embraces. But none of them seemed to attract the attention of the *Chronicle*'s photographer who, having finished taking pictures of the other two couples, now turned his attention to the closely entwined figures of Leo and Alex.

Long after the music stopped, they remained locked together on the floor. And it was only the bright, blinding flash of the camera which jerked them sharply back to reality.

Swearing violently under his breath, and practically

grinding his teeth with rage as he saw that he and Alex
were being viewed with some considerable ribald
amusement by well over two hundred people, Leo
quickly took hold of Alex's wrist, and swiftly towed her
off the dance floor.

'What in hell do you think you're doing?' Alex
panted, barely able to keep up with the stride of his tall
figure as Leo hauled her out of the ballroom and into a
small, deserted anteroom.

'If you think I'm impressed with these caveman tac-
tics, you're very much mistaken!' she ground out, rubbing her sore wrist and glancing down at the bare skin
of her upper arm, certain that she could see bruises form-
ing where Leo had gripped her so fiercely earlier out in
the hotel foyer.

'This "me Tarzan—you Jane" attitude doesn't impress me, you know,' she added defiantly as Leo paused
to slam the door shut behind him before advancing menacingly across the floor towards her.

'Believe me, I've got far better things to do than try
to impress a dyed-in-the-wool troublemaker like you,'
he snarled dangerously. 'You've really enjoyed yourself
this evening, haven't you, Alex?'

'Yes…yes, actually I have,' she retorted, raising her
chin and refusing to be intimidated by the angry figure
looming over her. 'And it serves you right!'

'Oh, it does, does it?' he snorted with fury. 'Well, if
it makes you feel any better—I'm quite willing to agree
with you.'

Puzzled by this sudden volte-face, Alex frowned, almost wincing at the glimpse of terrible rage in his glinting green eyes.

'Yes, it definitely serves me right. Because I already

knew that you were trouble with a capital T, didn't I? Right from the very first moment you appeared in my office. I should have taken to the hills as fast as I could.'

He gave a dry, caustic bark of laughter. 'And no one can say I didn't have fair warning. Because you even told me yourself that your name was Nemesis! So... maybe you can also tell me why I was such an idiot as to have anything more to do with you. Because I'd *dearly* like to know why I've been so insane!' he thundered, waving his arms angrily in the air for a moment, and then beginning to pace furiously up and down the room.

'For goodness' sake! There's no need to yell at me like this,' Alex snapped.

'As far as you're concerned—I feel quite free to do anything I like!' he roared, his temper now quite clearly out of control. 'I *really* thought that we'd got it together. That I had, after all these years, been finally reunited with the girl of my dreams. And, after that wonderful night we spent together, I was quite certain of it.' He spun around to glare at her. 'Poor fool, me—huh?'

'But...but, Leo...'

'Once again, you're quite right, Alex,' he grated bitterly. 'The word "but" should have been printed in capital letters—certainly as far as *our* relationship was concerned. Because you didn't care what you did—or who you hurt—in the pursuit of your stupid story. You didn't know Fiona. So why should you give a toss about her problems? After all, *you* simply had a job to do, right?

'So, why should you know or care that it was Ethel who tipped off the newspapers, hoping to put public pressure on me to marry her daughter? Why should you be interested in the fact that poor Fiona—admittedly a rather weak personality—dreaded being hounded into an unwanted marriage? Or that the net result of your article would likely make it even harder than ever for Fiona and I to escape the machinations of Ethel Bliss? And I was fair game, too, wasn't I?'

'That's not true,' Alex protested.

'Oh, yes, it is!' he stormed, pacing up and down the room once more. 'It only needed just *one* comment from a hack journalist—who's clearly got a mind like a sewer!—and you had the fact that I was a raving Casanova firmly planted in your brain.'

He spun around on his heel to glare at her. 'For God's sake, Alex. I'm thirty-one years of age. Did you *seriously* expect me not to have had any girlfriends in the past? Or do you think that I should have shut myself up in a monastery?'

There was a sudden noise of laughter and giggles out in the corridor, and the door was suddenly thrown open.

'I say...' a young, fair-haired man enquired. 'Have any of you people seen my girlfriend, Rachel?'

'*Get out!*' Leo growled, not bothering to turn around as he continued to gaze sternly down at Alex.

There was a brief gasp before, with muttered apologies, the young man quickly vanished from sight, softly closing the door behind him.

'To sum up what I was saying, when we were so rudely interrupted,' Leo continued grimly. 'You were *never* a "notch on my bedpost", Alex. The truth is, that after only one night of passion—please note, I did say *only one* night—I realised that I was deeply in love with you. That you were the girl I wanted to marry. But I now see that I was living in a fool's paradise.'

Leo gave a heavy sigh. 'You're clearly incapable of

understanding that a relationship means nothing—' he snapped his fingers contemptuously in the air '—if one of the persons involved either doesn't know or refuses to learn the meaning of trust.'

He stared silently down at the girl for a moment, noting the hectic flush spreading over her cheeks and the fact, for once, she didn't seem to have anything to say.

'So silent? Well, that *does* make a change!' he ground out sarcastically. 'You're a very rich and clearly a very spoiled young girl. Maybe you don't realise that I do actually take my job very seriously indeed. And when, after a brief meeting at the bank early last Friday morning, I found myself having to jet off to America with little or no warning, I—poor fool!—assumed that if you didn't immediately hear from me you'd realise that I'd get in touch with you as soon as I could. Unfortunately, as it turned out, I unexpectedly found myself in a large, remote estate in Connecticut with no telephone to hand.

'Bankers don't just count money,' he told her sternly. 'They are often used as honest brokers when two large corporations are thinking of merging. And that's exactly what happened last week. All the telephones had been barred, to prevent any of the principals trying to make a killing on Wall Street, and it was only by a lot of special pleading on my part that I managed to get hold of a mobile phone in order to try and make a brief call to you. And, raving idiot that I am, I also persuaded the principals to let me leave ahead of everyone else. So that I could catch a flight on Concorde and be back in time to appear at this damned ball. All these efforts designed, purely and simply, not to let you down.'

Alex had never realised what the expression 'ready to sink through the floor' meant, but she now definitely had a good idea. As the frozen ice around her heart began cracking and melting away, she was forced to acknowledge that Leo had been quite right. She *hadn't* trusted him.

'Where...where is Fiona?' she muttered in a small voice.

Leo shrugged. 'With her vet, presumably.'

'Her...what?' Alex frowned in puzzlement.

'The veterinary surgeon who looks after her horses.' Leo gave another heavy sigh, the anger seeming to drain out of his tall figure as he strolled across the room to stare out of the heavily draped window at the headlights of the traffic cruising up and down Park Lane.

'Fiona never wanted to marry me—or anyone else, for that matter. But the poor girl was saddled with a heavily ambitious mother, and I felt deeply sorry for anyone who had to live with Ethel Bliss. Unfortunately, Ethel took it into her head to imagine that I would be the perfect husband for her daughter. And, although Fiona and I could have sorted everything out quite simply between ourselves...we hadn't counted on Ms Alexandra Pemberton jabbing her long nose into our business.'

'I didn't realise...I didn't know—'

'But Ms Pemberton—a rich, spoilt young journalist— was solely intent on her story,' Leo continued, ignoring her interjection. 'Why should she care if her driving urge to gather material for her article could only further Ethel Bliss's ambitions? In fact, by the time Ms Pemberton had made a thorough nuisance of herself, the proposed marriage was fast becoming a *fait accompli*.'

'Oh, Leo...I'm so very sorry,' Alex moaned.

'So, it's fortunate,' he continued grimly, 'that as it

turns out Ms Pemberton *did* do poor Fiona a good turn, after all. You remember the vet, I mentioned earlier…?' He turned around to gaze sardonically at Alex.

'Well, it seems that he had been harbouring a deep but silent passion for Fiona. After reading your article last Saturday, the veterinary surgeon lost his rag, rushed over to see Fiona, declared his undying love—*and* gained her father, George Bliss's approval—before carting the girl off on his fiery steed! Well…' Leo added with a caustic grin, 'to be truthful—he actually drove off his beloved Fiona in his trusty old Land Rover!'

'And…and is Fiona really happy?'

'Ecstatically so, I believe. After all, she has found a man who loves her and, just as important, someone who's prepared to stand up to her mother. George Bliss is all for the romance if it means his daughter's happiness, so—always provided that he can keep his wife under some sort of control—there's no reason why the two people shouldn't live happily ever after.'

'I'm so pleased to hear it,' Alex murmured, hesitating for a moment before adding, 'I…well, about us…you *were* quite right. I'm so sorry that I proved to be so incredibly foolish, so lacking in trust…'

'Please! Spare me the fulsome apologies,' Leo ground out, turning around and walking back into the middle of the room. 'It's taken some time, but I've finally learned my lesson. I won't *ever* make the mistake of trying to see you again, Alex. Do us both a favour, hmm? Just make sure you stay well out of my life in future.'

'*Leo…!* Please don't go. You know…you know that I love you, with all my heart…'

He walked over to the door. 'Forget it!' he retorted

as he opened the door, allowing strains of music to float into the room.

'Believe me...I'm gone. I'm history!'

CHAPTER NINE

Sunk in gloom, Alex leaned forward across her desk, resting her weary head in her hands, and wishing that like Rip van Winkle she could go to sleep for well over a hundred years. There seemed no other way in which she'd be able to escape what was bound to be a monumental, cataclysmic row with Mike Tanner. It was only because he was out at a meeting, and hadn't yet had an opportunity to look at the photographs of last night's ball, that she still had a job and a desk, in the *Chronicle*'s newsroom.

'Maybe he won't go bananas,' her friend, Tessa, the assistant fashion editor, said, trying to cheer up the heavily depressed girl.

'Oh, yes, he will,' Alex moaned. And Tessa, after a quick glance at the photographs concerned, agreed that the other girl's prospects didn't look too good.

'Still, never mind. Maybe they'll inspire Mike to start a "Page Three Girl" feature,' Tessa said, referring to the idea used by other tabloid newspapers to increase sales by always featuring, on the third page of the paper, different pictures of virtually naked young girls.

However, if Tessa had hoped to relieve the other girl's gloom with this mild joke, she certainly didn't succeed.

'Oh, *don't!*' Alex groaned, before rushing off to the ladies' room and being violently ill. A few moments later, sitting in front of the mirror with her nervous stomach churning like a concrete mixer on fast forward, Alex

172

knew that she had to face up to the hard facts of life.
Not only were her days on the *Chronicle* likely to be
severely curtailed, but she wouldn't be at all surprised
if Mike told her not to bother to come in tomorrow.

'It's all Leo's fault,' she muttered grimly, trying to
whip up her anger against the man who, from when she
was sixteen, seemed to have cast a blight over her life.
But her heart wasn't in it. With those terrible, final
words, 'I'm gone. I'm history', she'd known, from the
hard note of finality in his voice, that their love affair
was well and truly over. And that, through her own folly
and stupidity, she'd now lost the man whom she loved
with every fibre of her being.

To have him walk out on her, leaving her weeping
figure alone in the anteroom, would have been bad
enough. But it had been his sudden decision to add a
sort of postscript marking the end of their love affair
which had finally demonstrated the scornful, contemp-
tuous light in which he now viewed her.

As he'd opened the door to leave they'd both heard
the strains of a fast jive instrumental number, which was
currently 'top of the pops', the music and its dance steps
having taken the country by storm.

'Ah...I think I'm going to claim one last dance with
you, Alex,' he murmured, striding back to grab hold of
her hand, and then retracing his steps with her protesting,
tearful figure being towed along in his wake.

'Please...I don't want to...leave me alone!' she cried.
But all to no avail.

'Come on, Alex! We mustn't disappoint your public,'
he drawled in an ominous, sardonic voice, a malevolent
expression on his handsome face as he paused in his

determined progression towards the dance floor to tap Sid on the shoulder.

'I think there's time for just a few more pictures,' he told the photographer.

'Well…I dunno…'

'Just do as you're told!' Leo snapped angrily, before hauling her still protesting figure onto the dance floor.

'All right, guv. Anything you say,' Sid muttered, quickly deciding not to argue with a man who had such a nasty glint in his eye, and who also dwarfed the photographer by a good six inches.

'If this is your idea of a joke, I don't get it,' Alex cried, desperately trying to struggle away from Leo's firm grip.

'Oh, you will, my darling. Believe me—*you will*!'

And, alas, she had.

The new dance had seemed to consist of being clasped firmly to the partner's chest, before being whirled away to the length of his arm and, just as rapidly, being twirled back again. Unfortunately, on the third 'twirl', Alex and her dress had parted company, with the red crimson satin gown continuing to go one way…while she'd gone quite another! And the resulting photographs were now lying on Mike Tanner's desk.

Shocked and stunned, she'd hardly known what had been happening to her as Leo had crushed her now top-less figure to his hard chest. After claiming her lips in one last, burning kiss, he'd whipped a tablecloth from a nearby table. Amidst the noise and clatter of broken glass and cutlery—not to mention the screams of anger and outrage from the people sitting there—he'd thrown the large white cloth over her bare breasts, before abruptly turning on his heel and stalking off the floor.

If it hadn't been for Sophie, Alex was quite convinced that she would have expired there and then from utter mortification. However, her friend had immediately rushed to her rescue, murmuring comforting words as she'd led the sobbing girl from the room.

It was Sophie who'd quickly organised a taxi, putting a warm arm around the still tearful girl as they'd arrived back home, and had also helped to put Alex to bed.

Quite how she'd managed to force herself into work this morning, Alex didn't know. The only faint spark of pleasure so far had been the bubbling happiness and joy of Susan's voice on the telephone. Was it due to the fact that, possibly for the first time in her life, Susan had defied her mother? Or that the older woman now realised that in her future son-in-law she had a man who was prepared to put his foot down? Whatever the reason, Susan's mother had welcomed her back from the dance with open arms, apologising for having upset Nigel, and promising to be less heavy-handed about their wedding arrangements in future.

Well, at least one couple was happy, she thought, looking glumly at herself in the mirror, and almost shuddering at the sight of her pale face and the deep shadows beneath her tired, dull blue eyes. She already knew that trying to forget her brief love affair with Leo was going to be a total waste of time. Because, although what had happened last night had without doubt been *the* most humiliating moment of her life, it still didn't seem to make an ounce of difference to how she felt about him. And, if she now found herself deserted, it was entirely her own fault.

After all, she *had* written that article which he, in his own way, had obviously found just as degrading and

embarrassing as the way he'd finally treated her. In fact,
Alex could find no excuse for her own behaviour. Right
from the moment she'd placed her finger on his picture
in the newspaper, and told a bare-faced lie about being
able to easily gain his co-operation, she'd obviously got
everything she deserved. As you sow, so shall you reap,
she told herself sorrowfully, before bracing herself to go
back to the newsroom and the expected summons from
Mike Tanner.

It wasn't long in coming.

'*Alex…!*' Mike's voice rang like a Tannoy around the
newsroom. 'Get yourself in here—*immediately*!'

Feeling as though she was taking the walk to the scaf-
fold, Alex took a deep breath and tried to concentrate
on putting one foot in front of the other as she made her
way towards Mike's office.

As if to rub even more salt in her wounds, she discovered on entering the room that Imogen Hall-Knightly
was also present, a happy grin etched on her thin features, and clearly looking forward to the pleasure of
hearing and seeing Alex's dismissal from the *Chronicle*.

'I want to know what the hell has been going on,'
Mike growled, flicking a hand towards the photographs
spread on his desk. 'You told me everything was set up
for the grand finale of our feature, with all the couples
at this St Valentine's Day Ball. And what do I find? Not
only has one bloke lost his girlfriend somewhere along
the line, but that you, Alex, have clearly decided to take
her place!'

'It's just the sort of thing that stupid girl would do,'
Imogen commented sourly.

'Do you think our readers are blind?' Mike continued,
ignoring the other woman's interjection. 'Even *they*

won't be able to help noticing that this guy, Leo Hamilton, seemed to have a dark girlfriend in last week's issue and has a new blonde one in tomorrow's supplement. And it's not just a girlfriend at the dance, is it? It's his damned stepsister—who also happens to be one of our reporters!'

'I can explain, Mike…'

'I should jolly well hope you can!' he ground out angrily.

'Well, the thing is, you see…' Alex muttered, before taking a deep breath. Staring fixedly at the wall above his head and ignoring Imogen Hall-Knightly, she made a full and frank disclosure of everything that had happened since the editorial meeting just under two weeks ago, haltingly at first, and then gathering pace.

'I've got no excuse to offer, Mike,' she said at last with a heavy sigh. 'I was just so blinkered, so determined to get a story…'

'I don't have a problem with *that* attitude.' He shrugged. 'It's *the* one important quality which journalists must have, if they're to succeed in this profession.'

'Yes, but not at the expense of other people's feelings. And I should have been honest with you. I should *not* have promised something that I couldn't deliver.'

Imogen Hall-Knightly gave a shrill laugh. 'I couldn't have put it better myself. It's obvious that you were simply never up to the job,' she added with a satisfied smirk. 'You'll never get a job in Fleet Street after this.'

'Excuse me, Miz All-Nightly, but I don't think we are discussing the *whole* of Fleet Street,' Mike interjected quickly. 'My only interest is in *this* newspaper. And the point at issue is what we're going to be putting in tomorrow's supplement, right?' he added crushingly.

Imogen, who wasn't a total fool, quickly nodded her agreement and lapsed back into silence.

'Any ideas, Alex?' Mike turned to face the pale girl standing in front of his desk.

She shook her head. 'No, not really. Sid took pictures of the two other couples, of course, and they're both still happy together, thank God.'

'Yeah. But what are we going to do about you and what's-his-name? And no, I'm *not* referring to those frankly rude photos,' Mike added grimly. 'This is still a family newspaper, thank God. You'll be pleased to know that I have personally destroyed all copies and the negatives.'

Alex could feel her knees almost giving way as she sagged with relief.

'I wouldn't look too happy too soon.' Mike's warning voice brought her sharply back down to earth. 'There's still no getting away from the fact that the only other pictures we've got of you and Leo Hamilton seem to consist solely of you two clasped in each other's arms,' he ground out irritably, lifting one of the photos from his desk and brandishing it in front of her. 'And there's no way we can pretend that that's Fiona Bliss, right?'

'We'll just have to scrap the whole photo shoot,' Imogen broke in quickly, taking the photograph from Mike's hand and looking at it with a curling lip before tossing it back down on his desk. 'Alex may have enjoyed herself last night, but there's no way we can use that.'

'I hate to say it—but you're right,' Mike agreed with a shrug. 'So I suggest we run that piece on that singer-songwriter, Alice what's-her-name, and how she's decorated her new home, together with... *What the heck's going on?*' he suddenly demanded, raising his voice to be heard over the loud altercation going on outside the door of his office.

A moment later the door burst open...and Leo Hamilton strode into the room.

'I told him 'e couldn't come in here, Mr Tanner. I told 'im to hop it, like you always said I was to do wiv strangers,' a young office boy called out, giving Leo's tall figure a wide berth and scampering across the room to stand panting in front of the editor's desk. 'I tried. I really did try and stop him, Mr Tanner. But 'e hit me! Look...' He pointed to one of his ears. 'He hit me—'e *did*!'

'I'll cheerfully box your ears again if you ever dare to be so insolent,' Leo drawled, clearly dismissing the young man from his mind as he turned to survey the occupants of the room. 'And you must be Mike Tanner, I presume?' he said, gazing at the short, bulky figure sitting behind the desk.

'Got it in one,' Mike acknowledged, before jerking his head at the boy and telling him to get out. 'While you, I take it, are Mr Leo Hamilton...?' Mike added, leaning back in his chair, calmly puffing on his evil-smelling cigar.

'That's not too difficult to deduce, since you seem to have my photographs spread all over your desk,' Leo replied coolly.

'Yeah, so I have.' Mike wheezed with laughter. 'Looks like you had some fun last night, doesn't it?'

While this exchange was going on, Alex was standing rooted to the floor, completely unable to believe her eyes. Leo...*here*? What on earth was going on? He'd made it absolutely one hundred per cent crystal-clear that he never, *ever* intended to have anything to do with her again. And now…marching into this office as if he owned it…?

'Would somebody like to tell me what's going on?' Imogen demanded, staring fixedly at Leo as though he were some sort of alien life form, before getting out of her chair.

'I think we've spent quite enough time over this bourgeois, sentimental nonsense of St Valentine's Day,' she continued in a firm, lecturing tone of voice. 'The fact that Alex's sibling was clearly sexually harassing her last night is surely not our business? Other than suggesting that the stupid girl clearly needs to talk out her problems—mainly concerning her own self-worth and her definition of herself in terms of her personal appearance—can I suggest that we get on with some rather more important items for today's issue?'

While Imogen had been speaking, Leo had been gazing at her with dawning horror. 'Good heavens!' He turned to Mike. 'Does this woman *always* go on like that?'

''Fraid so. Very politically correct is our Miz All-Nightly!' Mike grinned.

Leo shook his head. 'I don't know how you manage to put up with it.'

'To tell you the truth, mate, neither do I,' the editor agreed. 'All right, Imogen—you can push off now. I'll go through those other items in about ten minutes. OK?'

With bad grace, Imogen strode grimly out of the room. Following her departure there was a long silence, only finally broken by Mike's heavy sigh. 'Well, I'm no fool. I reckon you must have come to try and get hold of those naughty photos. Right?'

'You're quite correct,' Leo agreed, a faint flush rising over his cheekbones as he avoided Alex's eye. 'I behaved in an abominable manner last night. And, while I do of course understand that those photographs will have a certain market value—as far as this, or any other newspaper may be concerned—I am quite willing to make a financial settlement with the *Chronicle*, because I am most anxious to…'

'Relax!' Mike announced, holding up his hands to halt Leo's words. 'I've already destroyed both them and the negatives.' He paused for a moment, his busy, inquisitive eyes darting back and forth between the pale-faced girl and the tall, handsome and clearly uncomfortable man.

'So…' Mike said at last, 'Like I said, you've been a busy lad. Worked out which one you're going to marry yet, have you?'

'Of course I have—like you, I'm not entirely a fool,' Leo snapped. 'I've been in love with this damned girl since she was sixteen. So it looks like I'm stuck, doesn't it? That's if she'll have me, of course,' he added, finally turning around to face Alex.

'Can you forgive me?' he asked softly, walking over to take her hands in his. 'I'm desperately sorry about last night. Quite honestly, my darling, I'm just so madly in love with you that I can't even see straight any more.'

'Oh, *Leo*…! That makes two of us,' she sighed happily as his strong arms closed slowly about her trembling figure. Holding her tightly against his hard chest, the strong beat of his heart echoing her own, he lowered his dark head as his lips possessed hers in a kiss of total commitment.

They were only recalled to the reality of time and

place by Mike's dry remark, 'Don't mind me, folks! It's only *my* office, after all.'

'Oh, I'm sorry…' Alex gasped, quickly lifting a hand to smooth down her hair. 'I quite forgot where I was for a moment…' she began, before catching the amused glint in Leo's eyes, and bursting into laughter. 'Oh, dear—I never thought I'd be proposed to in a newspaper office!'

'Well, there you go!' Mike said, rubbing his hands together happily. 'You never know when things are going to turn out for the best, right? So, Alex, it looks as though we *have* got a story after all. Well…?' he barked as she stared at him in confusion. 'You'd better get on and write it up, hadn't you? We'll think about the headline later, of course,' he added, leaning back in his chair and gazing up at the ceiling. 'Maybe something along the lines of, "Banker Turns Down Heiress to Wed Journalist", or "Chronicle's Journalist Gets Her Man".'

'Over my dead body!' Leo snapped.

'Now, see here…'

Leo shook his head. 'I couldn't care less what stupid headline you use,' he told the editor firmly. 'But my new fiancée and I are off to buy a wedding ring. So, if you want the story,' he added, clasping hold of Alex's hand and drawing her after him towards the door, 'you can damn well write it yourself!'

'Are we really going off to buy a ring?' Alex asked as Leo ushered her into the passenger seat of his silver-grey Porsche, which he'd parked outside the newspaper building.

'Eventually, I'm quite sure we shall,' he laughed. 'But just at the moment, my darling Alex, I have rather more important matters on my mind. Such as,' he added, letting in the clutch and roaring off down the street, 'taking you back to my apartment and making mad, passionate love. I'll probably think of some other items as well, but I think that will do for starters, don't you?'

'Yes…I think I could probably hack that,' she murmured with a grin, a slight flush on her cheeks as she leaned closer to his tall figure, resting her head on his shoulder. 'I really…I really am terribly sorry about everything I said and did last night,' she added with a heavy sigh.

'Well, my behaviour was equally bad—so I suggest we just forget the whole episode,' Leo told her firmly.

'Yes, but what about your mother? There's no way I can go on pretending to be Fiona, is there? And when she finds out the truth about you and me…' Alex bit her lip. 'Well, quite honestly, Leo—there's likely to be a nuclear explosion all over Mayfair!'

Leo laughed. 'Relax, darling! There's no need to worry. In fact, I think you'll find that Mother will be over the moon about our marriage.'

'You must be kidding! Even if I'm prepared to bury the hatchet about the past—and I can assure you, most sincerely, that I am—I can't see your mother managing to put everything behind her quite so easily.' Alex sighed heavily. 'It isn't just what happened all those years ago. How can I expect her to forget all the awful things I said at the ball last night?'

'There won't be a problem,' Leo told her firmly. 'I know my mother. And, believe me, she's going to be *so* thrilled not to be forced to have anything more to do with Ethel Bliss that she's going to welcome you with open arms. Besides,' he added with a grin, 'the fact that I'm marrying the heiress to the Rothstein fortune is bound to make her declare her undying love for her new daughter-in-law!'

Alex laughed. 'Oh, come on! Be fair. Your mother may have many faults, but she never struck me as being a mercenary sort of woman.'

Leo shook his head. My mother's a great believer in the adage, "You can't be too thin, or too rich"! And, I agree with at least half of that sentiment. Which is why I've always been on the lookout for a *really* wealthy girl!'

'There I was thinking that you loved me for myself,' Alex murmured in mock-sorrow. 'And now I find that it's just my money that you're really after…'

'Oh, yes—*absolutely*!' Leo grinned. 'When my uncle, Lord Hamilton, learns exactly *which* girl I'm about to marry—I fully expect to be appointed Managing Director almost immediately!'

'You rotten man!' she laughed, giving him a light punch on his arm. 'It would serve you right if I gave it all away to my favourite charity.'

'Well…knowing how keen you are on journalism, I'm surprised that you haven't already bought yourself a newspaper. You can certainly well afford to do so.'

'You're a banker—I hope you don't give that sort of advice to all your clients?' She grinned. 'I thought everyone knew that owning a newspaper was a sure-fire way of losing money? And in any case,' she added, more seriously, 'I haven't been a journalist that long. In fact, I'm still learning the trade. And, truth to tell, it doesn't look as though I can keep on working for the *Chronicle*. Not after everyone's seen those photos!'

'I'm more sorry than I can say about my behaviour last night,' he murmured. 'I know that I said we wouldn't talk about it again. But I had a sleepless night worrying about what I'd done to you. And, of course, realising that it didn't matter what you'd said and done. You were *still* the only girl for me.'

'Oh, *Leo*...!' she sighed happily as he brought the vehicle to a halt outside his apartment. 'I'm just so happy. I can't believe that after everything that's happened to us we've finally found each other once again.'

'And I'm *never* going to let you go,' Leo vowed as he got out of the car and came around to open the passenger door, before leading her into the building.

'My only request,' he continued as the lift surged upwards, 'is that you faithfully promise *never* to write about me in a newspaper ever again.'

'Oh, no, I've definitely learnt my lesson,' she assured him as they arrived outside the front door of his apartment. 'From now on, as Miz Imogen All-Nightly might say, I fully intend to control my tendency to imitate male power patterns—especially with my chronologically gifted husband...'

'Oh, come on!' Leo laughed as he opened the door. 'I'm only seven years older than you, for heaven's sake!'

'In future...' Alex continued primly, struggling to keep her face straight, 'I shall indulge in an explosion of bourgeois sentimentality—and concentrate on exploring the horizontal levels of physical attraction between the species.'

'If that politically correct mumbo-jumbo means that we're going to spend at least the next forty-eight hours in bed—I'm all for it!' He gave a wolfish smile. 'By the way, whatever happened to good, old-fashioned, love, honour and obey...?'

'I'll happily go along with ''love'' and ''honour''. But ''obey'' is *definitely* out!'

'I'm sorry to hear that.' He gave a heavily dramatic sigh. 'Especially as I was *really* looking forward to giving the orders around here from now on. For instance…I was just about to demand an explanation of exactly *why* you haven't already started taking off your clothes,' he added sternly, his green eyes gleaming with laughter as he propelled her swiftly towards the bedroom.

'Well…maybe we could make an exception for that *particular* request in future,' she murmured, giving a shriek of laughter as she found herself suddenly swept off her feet and tossed lightly down onto the bed.

'My dearest, darling girl,' Leo growled impatiently as he joined her on the soft mattress a moment later. 'Believe me—it's the here and *now* that I'm interested in,' he added, taking her lovingly in his arms. 'Now…and for ever.'

The London Chronicle Monday 25th March

JAMES BOSWELL'S SOCIAL DIARY

THREE VALENTINES—
AND A WEDDING!

READERS of this column—who learned only a few weeks ago of the upset at Lady Lucas's Valentine Ball, where her son, glamorous man about town Leo Hamilton, abruptly changed partners and decided to romance *Chronicle* journalist Alex Pemberton—will be pleased to hear that Leo and Alex, who were clearly very much in love, have finally tied the knot! In a simple but moving ceremony yesterday, Leo married Alex, daughter of the late racing driver Johnny Pemberton, and sole heiress of the Rothstein fortune. The bride, given away by the editor of this newspaper, Mike Tanner, was attended by an old schoolfriend, the Hon. Sophie Garner, and fellow journalists Tessa Kelly and Lizzy Holden. (See photographs of the wedding on pages 12-14.) Lady Lucas is apparently delighted by the marriage. 'I'm so happy for them both,' she said yesterday. 'I've known dear Alexandria since she was a young girl. I always knew that she would make the perfect wife for my son.' Leo and Alex, who has taken extended leave from the *Chronicle* for the time being, are on an extended honeymoon, discovering the delights of Australia.

MILLS & BOON®

Next Month's Romances

♡

Each month you can choose from a wide variety of romance novels from Mills & Boon. Below are the new titles to look out for next month from the Presents™ and Enchanted™ series.

Presents™

THE DIAMOND BRIDE	Carole Mortimer
THE SHEIKH'S SEDUCTION	Emma Darcy
THE SEDUCTION PROJECT	Miranda Lee
THE UNMARRIED HUSBAND	Cathy Williams
THE TEMPTATION GAME	Kate Walker
THE GROOM'S DAUGHTER	Natalie Fox
HIS PERFECT WIFE	Susanne McCarthy
A FORBIDDEN MARRIAGE	Margaret Mayo

Enchanted™

BABY IN A MILLION	Rebecca Winters
MAKE BELIEVE ENGAGEMENT	Day Leclaire
THE WEDDING PROMISE	Grace Green
A MARRIAGE WORTH KEEPING	Kate Denton
TRIAL ENGAGEMENT	Barbara McMahon
ALMOST A FATHER	Pamela Bauer & Judy Kaye
MARRIED BY MISTAKE!	Renee Roszel
THE TENDERFOOT	Patricia Knoll

H1 9802

PARTY TIME!

How would you like to win a year's supply of Mills & Boon® Books? Well, you can and they're FREE! Simply complete the competition below and send it to us by 31st August 1998. The first five correct entries picked after the closing date will each win a year's subscription to the Mills & Boon series of their choice. What could be easier?

BALLOONS	BUFFET	ENTERTAIN
STREAMER	DANCING	INVITE
DRINKS	CELEBRATE	FANCY DRESS
MUSIC	PARTIES	HANGOVER

S	O	E	T	A	R	B	E	L	E	C
T	E	F	M	U	S	I	C	D	D	H
S	U	I	V	Z	T	E	Y	R	A	A
N	E	N	T	E	R	T	A	I	N	N
O	B	V	E	R	E	H	K	N	C	G
O	J	I	F	O	A	L	R	K	I	O
L	M	T	F	V	M	P	U	S	N	V
L	P	E	U	Q	E	N	Z	S	G	E
A	W	G	B	X	R	C	T	B	Y	R
B	F	A	N	C	Y	D	R	E	S	S

C8B

Please turn over for details of how to enter...

HOW TO ENTER

Can you find our twelve party words? They're all hidden somewhere in the grid. They can be read backwards, forwards, up, down or diagonally. As you find each word in the grid put a line through it. When you have completed your wordsearch, don't forget to fill in the coupon below, pop this page into an envelope and post it today—you don't even need a stamp!

Mills & Boon Party Time! Competition
FREEPOST CN81, Croydon, Surrey, CR9 3WZ
EIRE readers send competition to PO Box 4546, Dublin 24.

Please tick the series you would like to receive if you are one of the lucky winners

Presents™ ❑ Enchanted™ ❑ Medical Romance™ ❑
Historical Romance™ ❑ Temptation® ❑

Are you a Reader Service™ Subscriber?   Yes ❑   No ❑

Mrs/Ms/Miss/Mr ....Intials ....
(BLOCK CAPITALS PLEASE)

Surname...

Address ....

....

....Postcode.........................

(I am over 18 years of age)   C8B

One application per household. Competition open to residents of the UK and Ireland only. You may be mailed with offers from other reputable companies as a result of this application. If you would prefer not to receive such offers, please tick box. ❑

Closing date for entries is 31st August 1998.

Mills & Boon® is a registered trademark of Harlequin Mills & Boon Limited.

MILLS & BOON®

Stories to make you smile!

Don't miss this fabulous collection of three
brand new stories that will make you smile
and fuel your fantasies!

Discover the fun of falling in love with these
humorous stories by three romantic
award-winning authors—

ELISE TITLE—ONE WAY TICKET

BARBARA BRETTON—THE MARRYING MAN

LASS SMALL—GUS IS BACK

Available from 9th March 1998   Price: £5.25

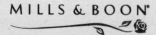

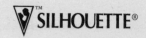

SPECIAL OFFER £5 OFF

FLYING FLOWERS

Beautiful fresh flowers, sent by 1st class post to any UK and Eire address.

We have teamed up with Flying Flowers, the UK's premier 'flowers by post' company, to offer you £5 off a choice of their two most popular bouquets the 18 mix (CAS) of 10 multihead and 8 luxury bloom Carnations and the 25 mix (CFG) of 15 luxury bloom Carnations, 10 Freesias and Gypsophila. All bouquets contain fresh flowers 'in bud', added greenery, bouquet wrap, flower food, care instructions, and personal message card. They are boxed, gift wrapped and sent by 1st class post.

To redeem £5 off a Flying Flowers bouquet, simply complete the application form below and send it with your cheque or postal order to; **HMB Flying Flowers Offer, The Jersey Flower Centre, Jersey JE1 5FF.**

ORDER FORM (Block capitals please) Valid for delivery anytime until 30th November 1998 MAB/0198/A

Title .... Initials .... Surname ....

Address ....

.... Postcode ....

Signature .... Are you a Reader Service Subscriber **YES/NO**

Bouquet(s) **18 CAS** (Usual Price £14.99) **£9.99** ☐   **25 CFG** (Usual Price £19.99) **£14.99** ☐

I enclose a cheque/postal order payable to Flying Flowers for £ .... or payment by

VISA/MASTERCARD ☐☐☐☐☐☐☐☐☐☐☐☐☐☐☐☐ Expiry Date ..../........./.........

PLEASE SEND MY BOUQUET TO ARRIVE BY ..../........./.........

TO Title .... Initials .... Surname ....

Address ....

.... Postcode ....

Message (Max 10 Words) ....

Please allow a minimum of four working days between receipt of order and 'required by date' for delivery

You may be mailed with offers from other reputable companies as a result of this application.

Please tick box if you would prefer not to receive such offers. ☐

Terms and Conditions Although dispatched by 1st class post to arrive by the required date the exact day of delivery cannot be guaranteed. Valid for delivery anytime until 30th November 1998. Maximum of 5 redemptions per household, photocopies of the voucher will be accepted.